ISBN   2-7214-5773-4

Distribution : *Librairie Orientale*
P.O.Box 1986, Beirut — Lebanon

Martha Sharp Joukowsky

The Young Archaeologist
in the Oldest Port City in the World

illustrated by
Fadlallah Dagher

 dar el-machreq SARL BEYROUTH

Acknowledgments

This book has been tenderly curated by Nina Jidejian, distinguished author of numerous scholarly volumes on Lebanon. I express my deepest appreciation for her patience, untiring skill and devotion. Without her invaluable assistance, this volume would never have been published.

Fadlallah Dagher was born in Beirut, Lebanon in 1961. He completed his studies at Notre-Dame College, Jamhour and earned a degree in Architecture at the Académie Libanaise des Beaux-Arts, Beirut.
He has shown unusual talent in drawing and as a cartoonist from a young age. His cartoons appear in Lebanon's widely read weekly *Magazine*. He is also responsible for the illustrations in a children's book entitled *Histoire Illustrée du Liban* by Nayla de Freige and Maria Saad, published by Larousse in November 1987. His favorite archaeological site in Lebanon since he was a boy has been Byblos, hence his interest in and his familiarity with the site.

4

Contents

Page

Author's Biographical Sketch 7

Chapter **1** 9

Arrival

Chapter **2** 19

The First Settlers
Neolithic Byblos 6000-4000 B.C.

Chapter **3** 27

Jar Burials
Chalcolithic Byblos 4000-3000 B.C.

Chapter **4** 33

In the Temple of Baalat Gebal
Early Bronze Age 3000-2300 B.C.

Chapter **5** 39

A Great Ash Layer
The Amorite Invasion 2300-2100 B.C.

Chapter **6** 47

In the Tomb
Byblos is rebuilt 2100-1900 B.C.
The Middle Bronze Age 1900-1600 B.C.

Chapter **7** 53

Isis and Osiris
Late Bronze Age 1600-1200 B.C.

Chapter **8** 59

A Phoenician Ship
The Iron Age 1200-539 B.C.

Chapter **9** 67

Sebastian
Byblos under Persian Rule 539-332 B.C.

Page

Chapter **10** 75

The Olympics
Hellenistic Byblos 332-64 B.C.

Chapter **11** 81

Astarte and Adonis
Roman Byblos 64 B.C.-330 A.D.

Chapter **12** 87

The Christian Church
Byzantine Byblos 330-636 A.D.

Chapter **13** 95

In a Cave
The First Arab Period 636-1108 A.D.

Chapter **14** 103

Embriaci vs. Bohemond
Crusader Gibelet 1108-1299 A.D.

Chapter **15** 111

Discovery in the Cave
Mameluke Byblos 1299-1516 A.D.

Chapter **16** 117

Excavation
The Ottoman Turks 1516-1840 A.D.

Chapter **17** 125

A Final Look
Modern Byblos 1840-Present

Chronological list of Princes and
Kings of Byblos 132

Glossary 133

5

Martha Sharp Joukowsky attended Brown University, obtained her B.A. in Classics from New York University, an M.A. in Archaeology from the American University of Beirut, Lebanon, and Ph.D., *Doctorat d'Etat* in Archaeology from the University of Paris I. She is Assistant Professor at Brown University and at New York University. She has been excavating archaeological sites since 1968, then at Tell el Ghassil and at Sarafand in Lebanon. In 1973 she directed the excavation of Neolithic Sham Wan, Hong Kong. From 1975 to 1986, she has been working at Aphrodisias, Turkey, and has published the final report of the prehistoric excavations. From 1982 to 1985 she has directed the field operations for the Brown University excavation of the Early Bronze Age site of La Muculufa in Sicily, and in 1987 the Kasfiki site in Corfu, Greece. Martha Joukowsky has authored numerous articles but is best known for her text book, *A Complete Manual of Field Archaeology*, published in 1980 by Prentice Hall. She is Trustee of the American Institute of Archaeology, member of the Society of Professional Archaeologists and a Director of the Association for Field Archaeology as well a member of numerous other archaeological organizations. The author is a Trustee of the American University of Beirut, Trustee Emerita of Brown University, and is a Director of the Center for Old World Archaeology and Art also at Brown University. She is married to Artemis A.W. Joukowsky. They have three children, and lived in Lebanon from 1967 to 1973, and in Byblos for part of that time.

7

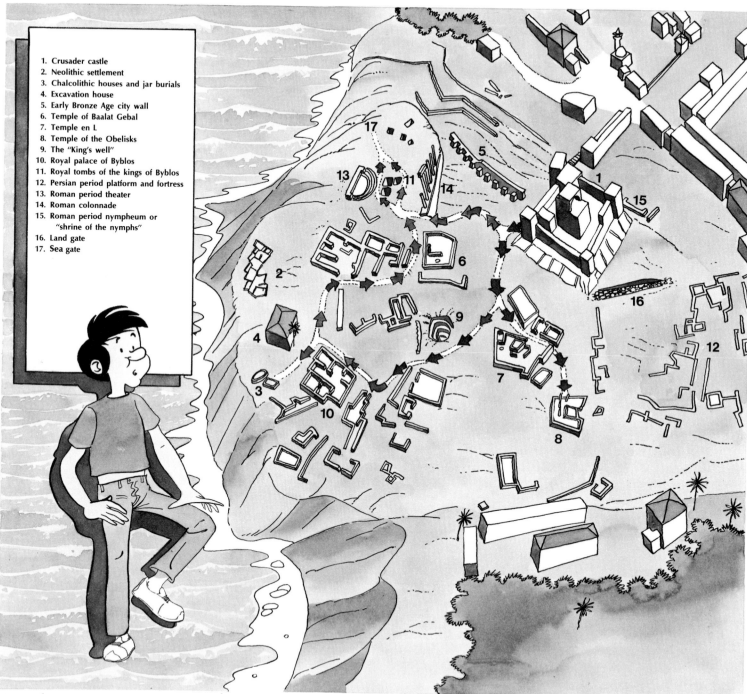

The legend within the image:

1. Crusader castle
2. Neolithic settlement
3. Chalcolithic houses and jar burials
4. Excavation house
5. Early Bronze Age city wall
6. Temple of Baalat Gebal
7. Temple en L
8. Temple of the Obelisks
9. The "King's well"
10. Royal palace of Byblos
11. Royal tombs of the kings of Byblos
12. Persian period platform and fortress
13. Roman period theater
14. Roman colonnade
15. Roman period nympheum or "shrine of the nymphs"
16. Land gate
17. Sea gate

Plan of the site of ancient Byblos with Sammy's path marked with arrows

8

CHAPTER 1

Arrival

"Do I have to go?" Sammy wanted to know.

"Your mother is needed to care for her parents, and I have to travel for business this summer," his father said apologetically. He was reasoning with both of his children, but it was already decided. Nina, Sammy's older sister, would go to camp, and Sammy would travel to Byblos, Lebanon, to stay with his Aunt Nadia, his mother's sister. It seemed to Sammy that two months was a long time to be away from home. It seemed like forever.

"Byblos?" he said. This was the first time he'd ever heard of such a place.

"Yes, that's where your aunt lives," said his father. "It's a charming old fishing town just 25 miles north of Beirut. Our people have lived in Byblos since before anyone can remember. Byblos is the Greek word for 'papyrus' which ancient people used for paper. The people who live there now call it *Jebail*. You've probably heard us speak about Jebail — but I love the old Greek name."

Sammy spent most of the following week preparing for his trip to Lebanon. He looked at maps, said good-bye to his friends, and several times he packed and repacked, packed and repacked. The boy was so excited he could hardly contain himself.

It was early in the morning on the day of his departure, when Sammy's father and sister, Nina, drove him to New York's Kennedy Airport. Mr. Canaan hugged Sammy, and Nina gave him a big bear squeeze. "Have a great time! Write! And be good!" they both said. Sammy hurried down the corridor to the airplane. Just before he entered, he

9

turned and waved a final good-bye. Again and again he rehearsed the directions his father had given him for finding his Aunt Nadia at the Beirut airport. He kept repeating them even as the stewardess escorted him to his seat.

During the first part of the fifteen hour trip Sammy was excited. But after he watched the movie, read, drank juice, and ate, he began to feel lonely. He was very tired, but too tense to rest. Pan American flight Number One left New York to follow a long route: first to Frankfurt Germany, from there to Istanbul Turkey, and then finally to Beirut, the capital of Lebanon. To Sammy, the flight seemed endless.

Some fifteen hours later, just before the jumbo jet touched down in Beirut, Sammy became worried and wondered, "Is someone really meeting me?" Although very anxious, he tried to make his face calm. Once on the ground, a stewardess led him inside, to customs where he presented his passport for inspection. After the official stamped his passport he walked through the barrier, and as he did so, he became aware of a stir in the waiting area. Suddenly a small woman exclaimed, "Sammy! I'm your Aunt Nadia! This is your Uncle Raymond. Welcome! We are your summer family!"

"My mother told me there's nothing more special than a Lebanese welcome," he said close to tears. He felt such relief to be found. Misty-eyed, he heard the custom's official behind him say "*Ahlan wa Sahlan*, you are welcome!"

Sammy greeted Aunt Nadia, Uncle Raymond and all the other family members. He felt somewhat bewildered by all the introductions, as each and every member joyfully embraced him. Aunt Nadia spoke rapidly to Uncle Raymond in a language he knew was Arabic, but Sammy could hardly understand a word. A bit older, Nadia was also shorter and more stout than his mother, but she certainly looked warm and welcoming. Sammy decided that it was her kind, accepting eyes.

The boy was directed to an old Mercedes by his Uncle Raymond. Peering eagerly out of the moving car, Sammy saw that Beirut was a bustling city filled with everything from sprawling, unkempt, corrugated iron shacks to sophisticated, modern hotels, high-rise apartments, and romantic-looking villas — all situated for rich views of the blue Mediterranean. Almost at once, the city was lost from sight in the scurrying traffic. Everyone seemed to be risking their lives behind the wheel, and there were endless starts and stops. It seemed to Sammy that Uncle Raymond was subjecting the battered Mercedes to unnecessary torture in pursuing their particular route out of town, but he tried to be calm. After a patch of untidy filling stations, factories that bordered the street, ship yards, and shops, the scene changed dramatically. He was surprised to find they were now driving along the sea. Even so, there was a continuous honking of horns, and bumper-to-bumper cars — all seemingly on the attack, zooming past them on the modern four-lane highway. Sammy was sure that the whole city was on the road, rushing here and there, and mostly past them, for his uncle was a very slow driver. Then suddenly, they were on a winding two-lane road which didn't look as if it were built to allow two cars to pass at all. More than once Sammy closed his eyes as Uncle Raymond, with his horn blasting, navigated hairpin curves. Sammy sure was glad to see the traffic beginning to thin out.

Before long they were speeding pell mell — now Uncle Raymond went fast — down the narrow ribbon of a road along a rugged shoreline backed by steep green mountain ridges. On the way, his uncle told him that this was The Lebanon, the marvelous mountains of history and legend. Sammy peered at all these wonders. He gasped as he looked downward into deep ravines that had been carved by swift-flowing rivers rushing toward the sea. Now they were only a summer trickle, if not completely dried up. Abruptly Uncle Raymond pulled the car over to the side of the road. He turned to Sammy, "Let's stop for a moment. I want to show you something. Wait in the car Nadia. We'll be right back."

"Where are we, Auntie?"

"About fifteen kilometers north of Beirut at a place called the Dog River — *Nahr el-Kelb*, as we call it in Arabic. Uncle Raymond wants to show you some famous inscriptions carved into the mountain rock face. Many conquerors have traveled up and down the coast on this very road, Sammy. It is a pathway used since prehistoric times."

Although Sammy was tired and not quite sure what his aunt was talking about, he felt it would be wrong to protest. He climbed out of the car, suddenly aware of a steep ravine that plunged into a narrow gorge almost at his feet! Sammy looked toward the steep walls of jagged rocks that stood above them. "Lebanon was under the sea for many millions of years," Uncle Raymond said. "Then limestones and dolomite were thrust up from the sea and became these mountains. About twenty-six million years ago, land forms began to be shaped into much of how they look now. But the final touch was created both by torrential rains and volcanic eruptions. These rains and strong winds carried rock and sand down to the coast, and combined with more volcanic activity left the small shelf you're standing on."

Sammy looked down at where he was standing, not quite sure he felt too secure after all that.

Pointing to the sea coast and then to the mountains, Uncle Raymond continued. "This rocky coastal strip is bordered by limestone hills rising some 870 meters (2500 feet). They're green now because we have had heavy spring rains. See those hills? They were snow-capped until a few weeks ago.

If we wanted to, we could swim or water ski, and snow ski in the same day!"

Before Sammy could wish he'd been here a few weeks ago, Uncle Raymond was off, motioning to follow him up a steep path. Slipping and sliding in his new loafers, Sammy braved the loose rocks that threatened to tumble him down at every step. Part way up the bluff, Uncle Raymond pointed, "There! There, Sammy, look there."

Following the line of Raymond's finger, the boy saw a rock face covered with the strangest kinds of marks he'd ever seen.

His Uncle began to explain. "Since 1500 years before Christ, invaders from many nations have stopped here to record their passage, their triumphs. Names like the Egyptian pharaohs Thutmose III and Rameses II, the Assyrian kings Esarhaddon and Nebuchadnezzar, and the Roman Emperor, Caracalla, who ruled between 211-217 A.D. — even the name of Napoleon III is inscribed on these rocks."

Sammy concentrated hard. Some of the names he remembered from school, but most of them he'd never heard before.

Uncle Raymond continued. "Look here, inscriptions written in Egyptian hieroglyphics, Assyrian cuneiform, Greek, Latin — and over there, French, even English! Each of these conquerors had his own culture and tradition. They each brought different ways of thinking, of doing things, to this land."

Far above the road, everything seemed so still and beautiful, and a soft breeze caressed Sammy. While Uncle Raymond commented on the various inscriptions and began to move down the cliff face, the boy mused about the road. If roads had memories, this one would have known the languages of all those centuries. He imagined soldiers marching through to distant lands, returning beaten or carving out their triumph here, on this cliff face. He felt a tingle of excitement race up his spine.

"But why is this place called the Dog River?" Sammy asked.

"Because tradition says that a large statue of a dog-god was built here. Whenever enemies approached, the dog would howl to give warning to the people."

Sammy was definitely impressed.

Sammy followed Uncle Raymond back down to the car, and took his place in the back seat. Aunt Nadia assured him that they would be in Byblos soon. On the road again, Sammy began to imagine seeing those armies, and traders with exotic riches, and settlers with all their worldly belongings moving along this tortuous road. Here in the comfort of his uncle's car, he was traveling along a pathway that had been used from ancient times. This same road had seen heroes and villains passing along it for thousands of years. Sammy decided that this bumpy narrow road symbolized the wear and tear of ancient and modern people alike. The modern noise of drivers blasting their horns seemed utterly unreal.

To the boy's left was the cragged shoreline and the green-blue of the sea. To his right were small coastal villages huddled between vineyards and citrus groves, with tiny red-roofed houses and their matching potted geraniums. Everywhere were umbrella pines, cypresses, olive, and plane trees. He hardly noticed the arched bridges over rocky river beds and the precious patches of cultivation. But the wild gorges winding their way from the near mountains down to the sea astounded him. He breathed in the smell of the sea. Already he loved this land.

Early in the hot July afternoon, they crossed a bridge over a small deep stream, and then they were in Byblos. Uncle Raymond pulled up beside a modest, yellow-washed house. Aunt Nadia helped Sammy with his things, and smiling broadly, led him into the cool, airy house and showed him a neat, comfortable room that opened onto a flower-filled balcony. Everything seemed pleasantly old — the house, his room, and even the furniture. There was little that was modern or fancy. Sammy put his backpack down, and looking out the open window saw something in the distance that intrigued him,

something he definitely wanted to explore.

Aunt Nadia offered him a cold lemonade. "Great! *Chukran*." Sammy responded in his one word of Arabic, "thank you". For a few moments he stood on the balcony. "A castle! That's what it is!" He shouted to himself. He rushed to find Aunt Nadia. "May I look around outside? This place is fabulous!"

His aunt smiled and nodded in agreement. Sammy put on his uniform — a faded red T-shirt, jeans, and tennis shoes. During the day the old town was busy and noisy with tourists, but now at sundown, they left, and the shops were closing up behind well-worn wooden doors. The narrow cobblestone alleyways that had been overcrowded with people, were now becoming deserted. He ran down the cobbled lane and off to what his uncle had told him was the ancient city of Byblos — the archaeological site.

Peering in, he found that he could just manage to wiggle under the barbed wire fence. He was amazed to see earth, piles of stones and fallen stone blocks lying amid summer flowers. On the far side of where he stood was that marvelous castle. After a few minutes he reached the side of its square-shaped walls. The castle remains looked gigantic, with its tall rectangular towers. Here was the fortress with its bastions, projecting corner towers, arches, and arrow-slits commanding the site on two sides. Its large moat faced sprawling modern Byblos to the north. Sammy followed the beaten path around the southern base of the castle, then descended into a lower area where the temples stood. From there another path turned west passing between ruins to the edge of the promontory which overlooked the sea and the sunset. The site was silent — it was all dreamlike.

Suddenly there was a sound: a stone rolling and next, the crack of a branch. Then all was still again. Sammy looked around. His senses told him that someone was close to him. But there was no time to be scared before he was seized from behind, a rough hand covered his nose and mouth, and he was savagely thrown to the ground. With the captor on top of him, he could barely breathe. The voice kept hissing abuses. As the threats continued, the grip lessened.

Sammy, with a muffled scream, pleaded, "Stop! You're hurting me! Don't!"

Choking with fury, but in a low voice, the man asked, "Are you alone? How did you come here? You have made a bad mistake. This is an archaeological site. You have disobeyed the order of the Department of Antiquities." With a snarl he released Sammy. "Get out of here, and mention this to no one, or I will turn you in. Hurry, go quickly, or I will hurt you."

In blind fear, Sammy obeyed. In the space of five minutes, he had stumbled his way down the promontory, across the site, and around the castle to the fence. At the fence, he looked back and saw the hulk of the man slowly working his way along the same path. Quickly, he scrambled under the fence and made his way to Aunt Nadia's house.

Sammy presented a pathetic figure of a tired-out, disheveled, trembling ten-year-old as he dragged himself up the stairs and into the living room of his aunt's house.

"I know someone who has been up to mischief," said Uncle Raymond as Sammy entered. Sammy was too terrified to care. He was paralyzed with fright.

After that scary adventure, Sammy watched carefully what was going on around him. After a week of poking around on his own, and meeting relatives, he had formed some opinions of his surroundings. He wasn't quite sure yet whether he liked the noisy modern Byblos, built along the shore road, but was too polite to say anything. However just beyond — past a jumbled series of shops, houses, and apartment buildings — the ground was strewn with remains of the present and the past. Blocks of mosaic, tiny pieces of glass mixed with wasted cement blocks, tin cans, scruffy plastic flowers, and strange old pottery fragments that for some reason sparked his interest. They seemed... so ancient. Sammy learned that the people of modern Byblos weren't interested in collecting such old things. But Uncle Raymond assured him that didn't mean they didn't take an interest in their past. They

were very proud of their heritage. Even after domination by many other peoples, the Byblites felt they represented the survival of their ancestors, the ancient mariners and merchants, known as the Phoenicians.

Aunt Nadia's house was in the old town just beyond the arcaded *souk* or market area — which seemed to be the center of local activity. Coffee and sweets were offered to visitors at any time, and lively conversations could always be enjoyed. It was all part of the scene. On his own, Sammy found a few steps from Aunt Nadia's house brought him into the central square of the old town, whose sleepy quiet was disturbed by sight-seeing cars and tourist buses from Beirut. The men of old Byblos who did not have jobs in the city were craftsmen or shopkeepers; the rest were mostly fishermen. They spent their free time listening to romantic Arabic music on the radio, playing cards, and *tric-trac* or backgammon. Most of the women were housewives.

To Sammy, the laughing children all looked alike and seemed so different from his friends in Boston. Aunt Nadia explained that they had to be clever and inventive to keep from being bored. There was little TV, and few summer programs to keep them busy. They had to amuse themselves during the very long, very hot summer. Luckily, most of them were 'employed' by their families and helped out in the fields or vineyards, on small fishing boats, or even in the tourist shops. Soon Sammy

had gathered around him several friends, which Aunt Nadia and Uncle Raymond referred to as 'the gang'.

Of the few thousand people who lived in Byblos, there were only a handful whose lives centered around the ruins. These soon became special to Sammy — the shop keepers, guides, and most of all, the archaeologists. A friend of the family, a man named Clovis, who was a Lebanese archaeologist, had taken a liking to this young American who seemed to want to know everything. Whenever Clovis had spare time, he relished taking the boy for walks in the old town, through the site, or along the pebbled beach. Sammy was overjoyed.

Clovis was a small man of about forty, with eyes that gave the appearance of bulging behind his thick lenses. Oddly enough, this seemed all the more true when his fingers played with his worry beads — his ever present toy that was supposed to calm him. He had been a member of the Byblos excavation team for years and Sammy's many questions delighted him. The second week he led the boy on a special archaeological tour of Byblos. While explaining things, Clovis pranced about as though he were a cheerleader encouraging the ruins to speak. Sammy was thrilled. He greatly admired

Clovis. He had thought that his uncle knew a lot, but this man seemed to have a million facts and ideas ready to burst from his mouth. Sammy felt awfully stupid beside him, but he trailed along happily wherever Clovis went.

One evening they stopped for an ice cream cone before visiting the site. After the closing whistle, the site was officially closed, but Clovis explained that as the archaeologist, he could enter whenever he liked. At sunset, after the tourists had all gone, there was no one at the Crusader castle, and they climbed its outer ramp and its inner sloping steps. Sammy felt like a knight in Crusader times, daring to venture into what might be an enchanted castle. They stood on top of the keep, and looked far out over the site, off to the mountains, across the sea.

Clovis had a dramatic flair which all the more heightened Sammy's own tendencies. The archaeologist waved his ice cream cone when he punctuated a particular point. Turning to Sammy, he bubbled with excitement, "Here you are, standing on the very spot that your ancestors, those pioneers of Byblos, settled some 8000 years ago! People through the ages have come and gone, and all have played a role in the life of this place — the oldest port city in the entire world!"

Sammy's heart throbbed when he heard Clovis speak. "As you can see, Byblos stands on a land crest that just hangs out over the sea. Its location was strategic, for it linked this port to other port cities, and the coast to the inland." Clovis pointed to the harbor. "This port was the perfect geographic gateway for ideas to pass from East to West." Clovis waved his ice cream cone and almost lost the ice cream. "Look at those beautiful crescent-shaped harbors. Not only could they handle more ships, but they could also accommodate them under different wind conditions.! That was very important in the old sailing days. Byblos' main harbor is one of the best, natural harbors of the Eastern Mediterranean. Think of it as a spectacular setting for contact between a whole series of great peoples... the Egyptians, Phoenicians, Assyrians, Persians, Greeks, Romans, the Crusaders, Arabs, Turks... and finally the French! All of those people have left a rich cultural heritage here. Over the years each settlement built up its own layer, and we archaeologists peel each layer off, just like the skin of an onion. The artifacts, the things that are discovered in each layer, tell their own stories of how the people lived."

Because he truly loved his work, Clovis was as excited in telling this tale as Sammy was in hearing it. Sammy plied him with questions, prodded him for more stories. He could never get enough and, happily, Clovis never tired of telling him.

Sammy asked, "How come people lived here for such a long time? Why is this particular spot on the Mediterranean the world's oldest port?"

"Well," replied Clovis, "there are several reasons. The earliest known people in the area lived in the rocky caves above Byblos. Then, about eight-thousand years ago, settlers moved down here because the water that man needed to survive was plentiful. They had discovered it gushing from a great spring. So there it was — a natural life-support system. People won't live where they can't find water. Also, the site's position: it's right on the coast. Here your ancestors could fish, and later they learned to trade and to travel."

Clovis knew just about everything about the site, and considered it his duty — an absolute commitment — to educate this eager American boy. And Sammy certainly didn't protest. Clovis experienced a tremendous lift of spirit. There was something so compelling about an awakening mind. It promised well for the future.

Turning landward, the archaeologist pointed to the site itself. He told Sammy that, militarily, Byblos had always been able to protect itself from sea attack because of its strategic position on the bluff; the land side was protected by great circuit walls.

For one fleeting moment, Sammy imagined those walls covered with soldiers. Gosh! I'd give anything to be able to live in Byblos back then — living like one of them, he thought.

Clovis quietly drank in Sammy's enthusiasm. He looked at him for a long moment, enjoying the boy's genuine interest for his beloved site. Then he broke into a laugh.

"You are wound up, aren't you? What an inspiration you are!" A feeling of warmth and pride swelled in Clovis. Trying to be casual, he gave Sammy a playful pat on the back.

As they climbed down the castle steps and walked up the narrow street towards home, the youngster became acutely aware that the old town had closed for the night. It was hushed. The merchants hawking their wares were gone, the copper pans had been taken in, the fruit stalls were closed. Even Sammy was quiet. Something was happening to him that he couldn't quite explain, even to himself. All he knew was that he yearned to know more about these ancient stones — and it seemed as if they in turn wanted to share their secrets with him.

In these first two weeks, Sammy had spent most of his time wandering among strange structures, 'his' beloved castle, and through explosions of flower blossoms that bordered the beaten paths of the ancient site. When Aunt Nadia asked him if he liked Byblos, he answered almost bubbling, "Are you kidding? It's fantastic! I'm learning stuff I never dreamed existed!"

Almost every night, as he tumbled into bed, he thought: Here I am, just an ordinary kid from Boston, actually living in an archaeological site — a place where real people lived for thousands of years. He fell asleep smiling with the joy of being in Byblos, and so proud to be a Byblite.

The lion hunt

CHAPTER 2   The First Settlers

Neolithic Byblos
(New Stone Age) 6000-4000 B.C.

Then one morning, Clovis beckoned Sammy to tag along with a group of camera-laden archaeologists. But soon the boy took off by himself, fascinated by the great castle that dominated the twenty-five acres of ruins.

Running along the inner courtyard of the Crusader Castle, Sammy hesitated at the top of that now-familiar long flight of stairs which led down into the mysterious looking tunnel. He paused to give his eyes time to adjust to the dimness. Then, with outstreched arms, he pressed his palms against the damp, stone walls and maneuvered down the steep passageway which led outside to a lower courtyard. It was a relief to see daylight again.

He walked along the worn path that bordered the high Crusader walls, then down more weather-beaten steps. He followed them down to come out far below the castle onto a small, grassy plain that was filled with ruins. He moved past rough foundations of excavated buildings and the still-majestic temple remains, and followed a series of ancient tracks until he came upon a crater-like opening deep and so vast that it was as wide across as Aunt Nadia's house.

For the first time he noticed yet another, a third set of ancient-looking steps circling down this huge pit. Curious to see where they would take him, he made up his mind to investigate. The going was tough — so many thorns and so much overgrown grass made it hard to pick out one stone step from the other. Finally the steps came to an end, abruptly, at a dangerous, sloping ledge. He inched his way down, and almost fell... managed to slide, then JUMPED to the bottom. He landed badly, and for a long minute just lay there. Feeling in one piece, he stood up and looked around. He was in a terrace-like area in the middle of which was a round, small inner opening that looked like a large hole. He made his way over to it, stared down, but saw nothing. Picking up a rock, he dropped it. After what seemed ages, he heard the faint echo of a splash. Yes, water was still down there... it was a well.

Curious, he looked up. He was surprised to see how far down he was. "Why, the original water level must have been about as high as a four-story building! This must be the very deepest part of Byblos, dug away for water," he thought to himself. So this was what Clovis had meant when he said Byblos had been such a good place to settle; if ancient people had a supply of fresh water, they could easily drink and water their plantings and animals. And later, when there was a city, the people would not have to go outside the fortification walls for water when they were under attack.

Sammy was suddenly overcome by the closeness of the air. How hot it had become. After what seemed hours, he climbed up again and found himself back on the surface, in the fresh air again. What a relief!

He looked around, and knew from Clovis' description that he was in the area of the Neolithic period beginning around 6000 B.C., the New Stone Age area of the excavation. He remembered the cool and peaceful shade of a pomegranate tree where he had once taken refuge from the hot sun. Quickly he located it and lay down under its branches on the summer-gold carpet of grass.

He imagined himself back in this Neolithic Age, the earliest of times for Byblos, walking over the same land as those settlers had, who first brought life to the place. Possibly they were his ancestors, and possibly it was they who had erected their homes on this very spot. After a while, he began to daydream... almost 8000 years into the past; back to a warm spring around 6000 B.C.

* * *

Kez, his wife Hata and their baby daughter Tof, were among the first of the strong-willed settlers to make Byblos come alive. Hata much preferred the idea of a new seaside home on the rocky ridge to their damp and dark mountain cave. Here her family would feel secure, for the area formed a natural barrier against wild animals.

"This is where we'll build our shelter," Kez exclaimed.

Working carefully, they constructed a rectangular mudbrick hut under which they first laid a course of stones so the mudbrick wouldn't melt away with the first rain storm. Then protective roofing of animal skins, reeds, and tree branches was carefully packed with mud. And after that the earth floor was thickly coated with crushed white limestone plaster. They built the inside carefully though most daily chores were done outdoors. The hut was to shelter them from cool night air and winter storms. As their last task, they built an outside firepit for their cooking.

Kez was a man of many talents. He could farm, raise animals, fish, and weave. He was expert at chipping flint stones which were used as knives for cutting and scraping, handy daggers, arrowheads and spear heads for the hunt. Hata shared many of her husband's skills, for a Neolithic woman had to know how to take care of herself and her family... especially when her man was away fishing or hunting deer or wild boar. She knew how to tend the vegetable garden and care for the goats and sheep. She enjoyed sewing and potting, and was able to fashion animal skins into clothing or containers for holding liquids. But most important, she knew the lore of healing with plants and herbs, which she had learned from her mother, and she from *her* mother.

After the family had been there a few months, Kez and some of the other men joined together to hunt down a mountain lion which had been seen lurking behind their little settlement. Walking out a short distance, they put out a lure of fresh meat, and then crouched down to wait upwind in the thick, prickly undergrowth. They didn't have to wait long.

"Fan out!" whispered Kez.

Quietly they surrounded the feeding lion, who was much too busy to be aware of his fate. But before the strike signal could be given, a sound caused the animal to lift his head, sniff the air, peer carefully all around. He came to his feet. Then he saw one of the men who had begun to move. With a roar that his territory was being invaded, he charged. The hunters, now the hunted, leapt out of hiding, yelling and whooping to distract the lion from their comrade.

"Stop him!" yelled Kez.

Refusing to be distracted, the lion headed straight at his victim, a man named Mesh who had frozen in his tracks.

"Stop! Ayee! Aghr!" Mesh saw the lion's claws slash toward him, heard the rip of his leather tunic, and fell, screaming as his leg was torn by the lion's teeth.

Kez threw his spear into the creature and leaped onto the surprised animal's back, his flint knife flashing, and stabbed him again and again.

Furiously, the men all tried to plunge spears into the lion's neck, sides, back — anywhere they could reach. The animal raged, clawed at them, and then finally sank down on his side, nearly dead.

"Come on, let's tie him up!" Kez was breathing heavily.

Working quickly, they tied the lion's front and back legs to a pole which one of the men had brought for easy carrying. That done, they hurried to the side of their friend. Weakened by loss of blood, and trembling, he murmured, "I owe you my life, Kez. Thank you."

A shudder passed through the others. Although Mesh was badly wounded, he was alive. "We've got to get him down to the village quickly," said Kez. Three of the hunters carried Mesh's limp body, while the others carried the pole with the mountain lion.

As they reached the huts, one of the men shouted, "Mesh is wounded! He's bleeding badly!" Hata told an older girl to run for her medicine pouch. While she waited, she took the leather thong from around her waist and tied it above the mangled leg to stop the bleeding. Once she had the pouch, she took out iris roots and dropped them in water that was by luck boiling in the firepit. She crushed clover leaves and hops, shredded a piece of alder bark, and put it all to boil in another pot. That done, she tenderly wiped the blood away with a piece of soft, absorbent fur. She loosened the leather tourniquet for a moment. As soon as the boiled iris-root liquid had cooled enough, she dipped clean soft fur into it and wiped the wound again. The iris-root acted as an antiseptic. She spooned out the pulp residue and packed it on the torn flesh, laid soft fur over it, and wrapped it all with strips of soft kidskin. Then she removed Mesh's tunic and was relieved to see that the tough leather had protected him. The sharp and dangerous claws had made no more than surface tears. She applied more iris-root antiseptic, then gave Mesh a hot tea of clover, hops, and bark to stimulate healing; and most of all to ease the throbbing pain and help him drift into unconsciousness. Sleep — the best medicine of all.

"They've caught the lion!" a boy went shouting through the settlement. That evening there was a feast. The beast was dead. Kez heard the praises of the other hunters for his bravery. Though embarrassed, he accepted the prizes of the hunt: the animal's skin and its eye teeth. Later that evening, he presented one of the teeth to his wife for her necklace.

"Tomorrow I'll start preparing the pelt," said Hata, "but I need some new scrapers."

"I'll sharpen some flints in the morning," replied Kez.

During the next few days, the convalescing hunter kept busy by tapering the lion bones for use as needles and fishhooks. When Hata wasn't dressing his wounds, she busied herself with scraping the lion skin with the fan-shaped tools Kez had made.

A few days later, shortly after daybreak, the men went off to mine flint in the cool, forested hills. Most of the women were planning to make pottery.

Before Kez left the settlement, he appointed a young man to stay behind as guard for the elderly and the small children. "We need someone here just in case of emergency." The young man looked annoyed and eyed Kez sullenly as the others hurried off.

Soon everyone had either joined the flint miners, the potters, or gone off to fish for the village. Young baby Tof was left asleep in the hut. Hata made her way with the other women and older children down to the nearby stream bed to collect clay. They would mix it with just enough water, knead the wet lumps to work out the air bubbles, then coil rings around and around, up and up to the size and shape of pot they wanted. After that, they would smooth the forms and leave them to dry, to be baked in the sun.

Hata suggested to one of the girls who was nearby, "Why not try to decorate a pot? Look, you can scratch the surface with a reed or a stalk or, even better, a shell." She showed the youngster how to incise deep surface designs in the hardening clay. The younger children helped too by carrying, oh-so-carefully, semi-dry vessels back to the settlement where they placed them near each family's hut. One of the children noticed the young guard muttering and cursing as he sat chipping at a piece of flint. And asked, "Why do you look so grim?"

"That's none of your business," the guard snapped. "Don't bother me!" he added in disgust. The spiteful youth got up to make his rounds. He kicked at a few pieces of smoldering wood that lay in Hata's firepit. Suddenly, a fresh breeze caught the embers and blew them towards Kez' hut. In seconds the straw in the mudbrick walls caught fire. Within moments the entire house was enveloped in flames. The panicked boy raced away, yelling for help.

The only other adult in the village was Mesh, the man whose life Kez had saved in the lion hunt. Hearing the cries for help, he realized Baby Tof's life was in danger. In spite of his pain, Mesh struggled toward the burning hut. Coughing and almost blinded by the flames, he inched his way into the inferno. Perspiration poured down his face. Frantic, he yelled, "I'll save you, Tof! I'm coming! I'm coming!"

Poor Tof was whimpering with fear and almost choked by the heavy smoke. At last Mesh was able to reach her. He cradled the baby in his arms and dragged himself through the suffocating billows, terrified they would be buried alive by the burning pieces of roof timbers falling about them.

"Just in time, we're out. We made it!" he almost cried with relief. Suddenly there was a mighty roar and the roof collapsed. With just space to spare, they had reached safety. CRASH! The burning sides gave way and embers covered the ground.

The sight of the smoke startled the flint miners. "Head for home!" one shouted. They threw down their tools and flints and rushed to the village.

In risking his life to rescue little Tof, the wounded hunter had repaid Kez for saving him from the mountain lion. While everyone was surrounding Mesh and listening to his heroic story, Hata sadly walked over to inspect the charred remains of her home. She stooped down to look at something that caught her eye. With an astonished cry, she stood up holding aloft one of the pots. Instead of being destroyed by the fire, it's color had changed to pink and had become rock hard! "Look, look! What a fantastic accident! My clay pots have become like stone!"

Sure enough, there was a benefit of the disaster — that pottery could now be made longer-lasting than ever. Being of necessity a very practical people, they each experimented with this new discovery and before long, everyone accepted it. All the villagers helped Kez build a new and larger house, longer by far than it was wide. With great care they fashioned a stone bench in front where they could gather and sit, and discuss important matters while chipping flints or preparing bones for fishing and sewing.

As time went on, many new arrivals joined the little group and the community grew and prospered. Kez became known as an important leader throughout the area, and Hata as an excellent potter.

* * * *

It was late afternoon when Sammy awoke. Quickly he got to his feet and searched the ground. He decided to look for clues in the overgrown grass that could be hiding something. A few steps away from the pomegranate tree was the long house. He was sure of it. Yes — here it is! All along here were the foundation stones. Pushing aside some tall grass, he found the bench! Its stones were gouged with long scars on the surface — a sure proof of its use! Sammy searched the area and actually turned up what looked to him like parts of a fan-shaped scraper, some knives, and other chipped stone fragments.

"Yeow!" Sammy exclaimed as he ran his finger over the edge of a blade. "Boy, is this sharp!" He had cut himself, but luckily it didn't hurt too much. He then ran his hand over coarser stones — the large ones that had been ground down smooth into mortars and grindstones for milling grain into flour — that would have then been baked into bread.

Later Clovis told Sammy that these were the inventions of the New Stone Age: pottery and stone

24

that was shaped by grinding as well as chipping. Clovis had said, "Man no longer had to chase his food on the hoof, but could settle down and grow it. Grow the crops and raise the cattle and build the containers to hold everything — bins, corrals, houses, and pots. For the first time he could rely on himself and not on the wild herd. That's why this period has been called 'The Neolithic Revolution'!"

So *that* was the big difference between the Old Stone Age, the Palaeolithic, and the New Stone Age, the Neolithic. Now it all made sense to Sammy.

Sammy sat alone till sunset and pondered about all this. What a wonderful feeling to sit here in this ancient spot in the late afternoon breeze, surrounded by the world of long ago. The guard's closing whistle suddenly blasted from the Crusader castle. He got up and walked quickly to the site exit gate. He went through the old town square, jogged up the narrow cobbled streets of the Medieval *souk*, past the blacksmith's workshop, and up the steps to Aunt Nadia's house.

Clovis, who was already inside, greeted the boy, "Sammy. I was just telling your aunt how you were discovering some of Byblos with me."

"All this shop talk will have to wait until after dinner," Aunt Nadia interrupted. "Now it is time to feed our archaeologists!"

"Clovis, please tell me what happened in the next age."

"Done!" Clovis said happily.

Aunt Nadia laughed and with mock sternness ordered, "After dinner!"

26

Chalcolithic jar burial of Shen and his dog Tor

CHAPTER 3

Jar Burials

Chalcolithic Byblos
4000-3000 B.C.

Early the next morning, drawn by an irresistible curiosity to find more clues to the past, Sammy made a sandwich of left-over lamb known as *schwarma,* on Arabic bread and slipped out of the house. He decided to enter the site via the sea cliff and investigate the area Clovis had called "Chalco-lithic." He told Sammy that this period had such a population explosion that it took in not only the earlier Neolithic site but spread over the whole ridge.

As the church bells rang, Sammy climbed the steep cliff and walked to where he had been told the remains of round houses and burial jars had been found. Kicking at some bits of pottery that Uncle Raymond had told him were called "sherds," Sammy realized that these were fragments of ancient kitchen things — the water pitchers, china plates, Dutch ovens, stainless steel pans, lamps, and storage vessels of their day.

Until the night before, when walking around the site, he had never heard the strange sounding word "Chalcolithic." Clovis had explained to him, as he pointed out the round houses, that it came from the Greek words *chalco* — meaning copper, and *lithos* — meaning stone. The Chalcolithic period, therefore, represented a transition between man's use of stone tools and weapons to those fashioned from metal — copper metal. It was a revolution in tool manufacture.

"From around 4000 B.C., these levels, these time layers, were filled with stone and bone tools," Clovis said, "but they also contained early experiments in metal-working. And we must remember that long after metal was introduced, man continued to use the old tried-and-true stone — if for no other reason than it was abundant, easy to work with, and cheap."

Sammy trudged along to the round house foundations, to explore. Once there, he pretended he was an archaeologist, closely examining the stones for clues as to how the houses had been built and trying to imagine what kind of people had lived in them. He happened to see something that looked like the rim of a clay jar, embedded sideways in the earth. He stooped and peered into it, and saw something white.

What could it be? he wondered, touching it — BONES, human bones! A burial? In a jar?! He pulled away weeds, trying to get a better idea of the size of the vessel. It was huge! Is this what Clovis meant when he described a *pithos* — a very large storage jar? Storage for a body, as well as grains or oil!

He poked around a while longer, wishing Clovis were there. Beginning to feel the July heat, he took a sip of water from his canteen. It didn't refresh him much, so he thought he'd get out of the heat and stretch out for a few minutes inside one of the round houses. He wanted to think.

Sammy knew by the whistle blast that it was high noon. Guards signaled everyone to leave for the lunch hour. Sammy huddled in a corner, hiding, so he wouldn't be seen. When he felt quite alone and safe, he pulled out the sandwich he had made and ate it with relish. He licked his fingers and then took another pull on his canteen. The heat was definitely getting to him. He began to imagine what the Copper Age was like, 4000 years B.C.

* * *

He imagined that, in the main harbor area of the large village, there was a small figure straddling the edge of a hollowed log boat. This was an eleven-year old named Zir who felt the need to be near the glittering water. His loneliness filled him and he wanted only to run to the hills and hide. But he knew his duty was to return to the village. Almost in waves, the ache of losing his beloved older brother hit him. As he hurried, half-stumbled along, he heard the haunting chant of the villagers and knew the funeral was near.

Was it really true? It couldn't be, it really couldn't be. His head throbbed with the unacceptable. Shen, his brother, was dead. Shen had been setting a trap for a wild boar just outside its lair when suddenly, out of nowhere, the raging beast charged. Gored to death, both Shen and his dog, Tor, were killed.

His mother and father, realizing the bond that existed between boy and dog, commissioned the village potter to make two burial jars: a large boy-sized one for Shen and a small one for Tor. Zir had watched him make them: before the clay was hardened and fired, the potter cut a rounded diagonal slab out of the shoulder of each vessel so that the bodies could easily be placed inside for the burial ceremony.

For hours, all the villagers held hands and chanted songs around the prepared grave. Zir stood hunched over, shivering almost convulsively. Able to peer into the giant jar, he could see his brother's body laid on its side, his knees were pulled up to his chin — curled up like a sleeping child. Semi-precious stones and the family jewelry of simple ornaments made Shen look radiant. His head was capped with a net of small red carnelian beads.

Bending over the jar, his mother carefully set beside the body three vessels: one filled with water, one with goat's milk, and one with grain. She did not want her son to suffer hunger or thirst on his journey to the after-life.

"Look at that!" The crowd murmured, jolted for a moment out of its collective grief. His father was placing a precious copper dagger in the jar. "In the next life, at least, my son shall be able to defend himself," he declared.

In the smaller jar, lovingly placed at the feet of Shen, was the furry lifeless body of Tor. Looking at the silent forms, Zir thought how lucky they were to travel together to the next world. As long as he could remember, his brother and his dog had been inseparable. During the cool evenings, Shen would sit by the fire with a contented Tor curled up at his feet, as he was now in death, listening with his head cocked while Shen played tunes on his reed pipe. Everyone thought there was something special between them; their friendship was legendary in the village.

Tor was one of the most beautiful dogs Zir had ever seen. It was Shen who had first found him. While on a hunting trip he had stumbled over the wild puppy, deserted and starving in a cave. He had carefully put the little creature in his pouch, and carried him home to nurse back to health. After that they were always together, sharing so much love and fun. Happy together, they didn't seem to need others to amuse them. They spent hours playing jump-across-the-streams, follow-the-leader, walk-on-hands or hind-legs (as the case may be), and chase-around-the-trees.

Now the pottery slab was being fitted into position over Tor's little jar. After being sealed with resin, the vessel was placed at the feet of Shen's body inside the larger jar. As the second jar was sealed, the hushed crowd stirred. Zir put it into words for all of them. "What a beautiful way for true friends to be buried," he stammered.

The boy and the dog had grown up together, and now, much too young, they had died together.

* * *

Sammy felt strangely sad and lonely. The site seemed terribly still. He had a hard time for a

29

moment remembering where he was. Then he knew. Tearing out of the round house, he headed back to the jar. An awful quiet was growing inside him. There it was — that huge pithos, and the bones!

Breaking out in a cold sweat, he half-ran, half-leapt, heading for Tewfik's coffee house on the edge of the ruins. To his great relief, he found Clovis there with his friends.

"*Marhaba!* Where have you been all day?" Clovis chuckled, "You know I saw a red shirt which looked just like yours sneaking into the Chalcolithic round house at noon time. It was funny to see a red shirt moving around all by itself!"

Sammy chose to ignore this remark and said,

"Speaking of the round houses, I think I found a jar burial near there this morning."

"It's possible. You know, nearly 2000 of them have been discovered here in Byblos during past excavations."

"Hmmm. You didn't find one with a boy and a dog, by any chance?"

"As a matter of fact..." Clovis looked at Sammy quizzically. "How did you know?"

Sammy, feeling back in the 20th century and much the better for it, laughed, "I've just a natural talent for that sort of thing."

Egyptian envoys bear royal gifts to Baalat Gebal, the goddess of Byblos

CHAPTER 4 — In the Temple of Baalat Gebal

Early Bronze Age
3000-2300 B.C.

A few days later, Sammy looked for his friend and found him supervising the excavation team made up of workmen, students, and specialists. The team also included a photographer, a surveyor, and an architect. Clovis told Sammy he could spare some time to show him the city wall and temples of the Early Bronze Age.

As they walked across the site, Clovis remarked that Byblos had been at its height during the Bronze Age.

"Why do you call it the Bronze Age?" Sammy asked.

"Well, by then people were using tools and weapons made of *bronze*. The Stone and Copper Ages had finally come to an end, and the Bronze Age was established according to the bronze tools which people were using."

"What is bronze anyway? I've always wondered about that."

"It's an alloy of copper and tin. That makes bronze much harder, stronger, more durable, and more efficient than just copper for tools. Unfortunately, it was also used to create better weapons."

They headed north toward what Clovis said were Early Bronze Age walls. Once they reached the walls, the two of them studied the design, which Sammy thought looked just like an upright sandwich. Clovis told him that in fact some even called them "sandwich walls." Two massive parallel walls of stone had been constructed, and in between them was one filling of earth and a second of rubble.

Their remains towered above Sammy, nearly ten-times his height.

Then Clovis astounded him. "What you are seeing is just the foundation. The original walls were much higher."

"Higher! Wow! They sure must have expected trouble."

Clovis led him around to inspect the interior buttress supports.

"How about gates? How did people get in?"

"They erected two entrances," Clovis explained, "a Land Gate and a Sea Gate." He waved his arm toward the port. "Bordering the city — by now, Byblos was definitely a city, a prosperous port city — on the northeast was the Land Gate. Farmers and shepherds who worked outside the walls, as well as land travellers, used that gate."

Clovis went on, "The Sea Gate overlooked the northwest harbor which was active with local fishing fleets and merchant ships from all over." He dramatically swung his arm to include the whole of the Eastern Mediteranean.

The two of them strode along the length of the wall to the Sea Gate where Clovis launched into a description of the Bronze Age port. "Think of it! Egyptian ships unloading cargoes of black diorite, rose red and gray granite, and black basalt. Also, exquisitely carved vases of white alabaster, almost every one inscribed with the names of Pharaohs — whichever one was god-king of Egypt at that time.

In their turn, Egyptian ships took on tons of giant sweet smelling cedar logs needed in Egypt which had so much stone, and so few trees. Many merchants came; they all wanted our cedar. It was cut right up there in those hills. Too much was cut; now there's hardly any." Clovis could get so very emotional about certain things.

He continued. "Here, in Byblos, men from all corners of the ancient world exchanged goods and, more important, ideas."

"Where did they come from besides Egypt?"

«From Mesopotamia, the land between the rivers; we now call it Iraq. From Syria, and from the island of Cyprus, which supplied the ancient world with copper. In fact, the word *cyprus* means copper!"

"What kind of ideas are you talking about?" Sammy wanted to know more.

"Oh, all kinds of ideas. Improved metal techniques and always, it seems, new ideas for weaponry. Ah, but most important of all was the concept of writing — the real mark of civilization."

"Writing?" Sammy realized he'd always taken it for granted.

"Yes, we have pretty good evidence that writing was invented by governments to keep track of export and import trade. Man's first attempts at writing came about by his making marks to identify his property. The Egyptians used signs called *hieroglyphs* and the Mesopotamians used a so-called *cuneiform* wedge-shaped script. In the beginning it was used only for business contracts, but then its use was expanded to include laws and literature, and much, much more..."

Sammy, noticing Clovis drifting off, tugged at his friend's sleeve. "What were the other inventions, Clovis?"

The archaeologist struggled back. "Ah, yes. Beautifully carved seals from Mesopotamia and Egypt, and the use of the upright wheel for transportation. It never did catch on much in Egypt; everybody used the Nile. The horizontal wheel for pottery manufacture was another new idea. Man could now start mass-producing pottery and, as usual, that brought the quality down."

They wandered down to the Early Bronze temple area which Clovis told him overlooked a small sacred lake used for priestly purification rites. "What a beautiful place for a shrine," Sammy said to himself, and immediately decided to explore.

Once inside the temple he was puzzled by its many rooms. One had a row of four huge basins sunk into a bench. Clovis told him the basins had been used to store wine.

"How did all this look so long ago?" That same question came to him over and over again. He began to speculate, to daydream, jumping from the modern, plastic, Atomic Age back to the Early Bronze Age. Clovis helped him jump with surprising ease into the ancient past — that long ago time.

"Let's pretend that we are in the port, watching an Egyptian ship unload its cargo. We're excited over meeting people from such an exotic and rich land as Egypt, we can't help but boast of our new temples; one constructed especially for our city gods and the other for our city goddess, Baalat Gebal."

Clovis led Sammy to the temple dedicated to the male gods. A large triangular stone was positioned at its entrance. "It's an obelisk, but much smaller than those in Egypt," our imaginery visitors would have said scornfully. "We would have explained proudly that our new temples are divided into three parts. Now here is the outer court where the people come to worship."

"You mean they don't go inside?" Sammy asked.

Clovis shook his head. "Oh, no," warned Clovis. They respectfully peered into the second part of the temple, the part that had inner rooms for the

use of priests and for storage of offerings. In hushed tones Clovis explained that the third part of the temple was the most sacred and secret inner chamber, a holy of holies, reserved for the gods. "Only the holy ones are allowed in there, and if we're spotted, we could be in big trouble!"

"What's inside?" Sammy demanded.

"No one knows but the high priest," Clovis replied. He added very solemnly, "Most likely there are sacred golden statues of the gods because that is where their spirits dwell."

The archaeologist then climbed the ridge and led Sammy to the second majestic temple, over-looking the sea-cliff.

"Here was the temple of *Baalat Gebal*. She was our city goddess and signified the sky, happiness, gold, dancing, music, and love. She was very much like the famous Egyptian goddess, Hathor. I think that both the goddesses were worshipped for the highest qualities of womanhood: beauty, grace, intelligence, and fertility," said Clovis, visibly moved. Both Sammy and Clovis explored the Temple of Baalat Gebal. Clovis reminded Sammy that the Early Bronze Age began Byblos' long history of being considered a holy city — right through Roman times.

Turning to the sea, he said, "That afternoon, we would have watched as our Egyptian visitors' ship set sail, its oars pulling to clear the harbor and then its sails picking up the wind for home." A sigh of regret could be heard escaping from Sammy as the imaginary ship and Egyptian tourists disappeared forever.

They walked together to the coffee house for lunch. "Ummm, *taboula* and *hommos*," Sammy said hungrily. After being served, the boy asked, "Can you tell me what happened at the end of the Early Bronze Age?"

Clovis leaned forward and his eyes lit up as he declared, "The strength of Byblos' culture survived, despite wars and invasions which lasted for two hundred years! And then Byblos once again rose to great prominence and prosperity!"

Sammy waited for more, but Clovis wanted to save that bit of suspense for another time.

Sammy and 'the gang' play Byblites against Amorites attacking the city

CHAPTER 5

A Great Ash Layer

The Amorite Invasion
2300-2100 B.C.

It was to Sammy's disappointment that Clovis had to spend three days in Beirut at the Department of Antiquities. All Sammy's questions about the destruction of the temple and invasion which finished off the life of the Early Bronze Age people would have to wait until his return.

During short daily visits, Sammy continued to examine the temple area and the fortification wall, looking for the reasons for its destruction. He read an old guide book about the site, but he wanted to know the facts from an archaeological point of view. Sometimes on his visits, he picked up pottery "sherds," those broken pieces of pottery that he found lying on the ground.

Missing Clovis to guide him, he went to Abu Hanna, the excavation restorer, to ask if the sherds had any value and how old they were. Abu Hanna, who looked like a little old monk, was usually intent on his mending. But he politely examined Sammy's finds, told him what he thought they were, and hinted they were worth nothing. But fishermen began bringing their netted odds and ends to Sammy until he had quite an interesting collection: ceramic handles, rims, bases, some mosaic fragments, even what looked to him like a few badly aged coins. All of these he added to his precious flints, which he discovered near the Neolithic house foundations.

By the third evening he waited with almost unbearable anticipation for Clovis. It was dark when the tired archaeologist arrived. "How was your trip?" Sammy greeted him.

Dramatic as ever, Clovis loudly sighed, "I'm exhausted! I feel utterly finished!"

They had a snack, and then the boy and the man stayed awake far into the night, talking excitedly about "the collection". Clovis studied each piece with care. "You might catalog these things," he suggested. He showed Sammy how to number each fragment, draw and describe it accurately, and how to put it away for safekeeping. Little did Sammy know what was coming.

All at once Clovis jumped up and with a look of anger growing on his face, began to speak sternly, "What am I doing to you? Collecting antiquities is wrong! There are legal restrictions against collectors! They are criminals, looters, vandals, felons, racketeers, scum of the black market!"

"What?" Sammy cried in disbelief. He felt hurt and at great disadvantage. He didn't understand.

The archaeologist realized that he had wounded Sammy's dignity, and with a calmer tone went deeper into the subject. "By and large, it is because of collectors that the theft at archaeological sites occurs. It is a dangerous business, Sammy. Antiquities thieves have been known to threaten, even to murder archaeologists to steal finds. You see, once a find is removed from its archaeological context, it loses its scientific value. It is like a person with his tongue cut out, unable to tell us of its use and relationship to other people, or things. The result is that we know less about the site and the culture that produced the object. In short, its archaeological heritage is lost forever!"

Sammy felt awful, and looked sadly at his collection. Clovis, noticing the hurt look in the boy's eyes whispered, "Legally, even these fragments belong to the government. The Lebanese Government requires a permit for us to work here. We are entrusted not only to control the excavation, but also to protect it. When you pick up even a broken fragment of something, it's wrong. Let's say later you lose interest in one sherd by finding a second one that's nicer. You then drop the first where you picked up the second. That first broken piece, belonging to the first place, would be mixed with the one you dropped in the second place — and that would further mix up the situation. The golden rule is 'look, but do *not* pick up or move anything when visiting an archaeological site'."

Clovis studied the boy and realized that he had hurt him. After a few moments of silence he said, "Sammy, I want to encourage you. What you have found on the beach has lost its archaeological meaning already. Don't be insulted by my carrying on, just beware of the realities of our world. Continue your exploring, collect only on the waterfront, catalog your finds and, whenever you want, we will deliver them to Abu Hanna to be entered into the register of excavation finds. In this way you will be helping us. The story of Byblos can be built with your hands, too."

With that affirmation, Sammy felt more comfortable and less like crawling into a corner like a thief. He tried to forget Clovis' anger, and once again found that his effort to listen was a real asset.

After just a few hours' sleep, Clovis came for Sammy at dawn as he had promised the night before. They hurried through the deserted old town, their footsteps echoing on the stone pavement. Finally at the site, they walked down to the fortification wall which Clovis told him might have been damaged by a Semitic people known as "Amorites" — nomadic conquerors from the Syrian desert.

"Between 2300 and 2100 B.C., the Amorites burned everything from Lebanon to Syria right to the ground."

"Wow! That's awful!"

"Yes, but that kind of disaster, quick and unexpected, is important for archaeologists because everything is left in the debris just as it was at the time of destruction! For example, the treasures of the Balaat Gebal temple were undisturbed because there was a great fire. The roof fell in. Few people had a chance to escape, or even to take anything away. Excavating is almost like entering a time capsule."

Hearing voices from the Crusader Castle, Clovis recognized Monsieur Dunand's — his boss and the Director of the Byblos excavation — and so he left the boy to look around on his own.

Sammy also heard familiar voices just beyond

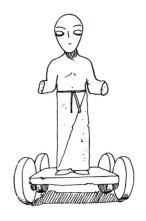

the city wall. Three boys from 'the gang' : bossy Jamil, who always wore dark glasses, quiet Wasfi, and the plump-faced baker's son, known as Hamid 'the monster', were motioning to Sammy. Once the usual greetings were over, he tried to have them figure out how the Amorite invasion had taken place. How could a wild desert tribe conquer a great city-state. How did they ever breach the tremendous fortification wall?

Sammy told the gang that no one really knew the answers, but they had to try to figure it out. He assigned roles. For the moment, Hamid was proud to be in charge of the Byblite troops. He had to think of the Byblites trying desperately to hold back the barbaric Amorites. Cool, talkative Jamil was assigned to be the Amorite Captain. Wasfi decided to just sit this one out. As they were leaning against the remains of the mighty wall, their magical minds carried them back to 2300 B.C.

Positioning his dark glasses, slicking back his hair and standing with his jaws and fists clenched, Jamil took over. "As the Amorite Captain, I am a strong, clever officer. I'm going to conquer rich Byblos, and do it in just one battle. I have only a few hundred, but very strong men, and we have traveled for a week to reach the Lebanese mountains. While camping under the protective cedars, I work out my plan of attack. After my scouts return with information about Hamid's Byblos, I decide to strike the city from four points at once: the Land and Sea Gates, plus two strategic points along the walls. Complete destruction of the city is vital for control. Jamil, I will drive your Byblites into the sea, if I have to!"

"How are you going to scale the walls?" Sammy interjected.

Warming up to the play, Wasfi hinted from the sidelines that it might be difficult to take the walls without being spotted — unless Jamil set up some sort of diversion.

"So I'll devise a fifth point of attack," said Jamil, "to be carried out from WITHIN the walls. Small detachments of my men will enter the city at dusk, just before the gates close, disguised as shepherds and farmers, their weapons hidden under their clothes. No one will realize what is going on until it is too late! When the attack is to begin, I will whistle a signal to my men inside the city to raid the temple treasure, the army headquarters, and, of course, the palace."

Wasfi thought that Jamil's plan might actually succeed. He said, "OK, according to plan, at dusk, small groups of disguised Amorites will walk casually through the gates, separate, and spread to all parts of the city and hide. One group will wait through the night crouching behind huge pithoi, those man-sized jars, in the palace storerooms."

This was too much for Hamid, who sputtered, "You mean that as Commander of the Byblos forces, I don't even know what is going on? That's not fair!"

Jamil interrupted, "Right! Just before dawn, I, along with a small troop of commandos, will quietly scale the wall by using log ramps and knotted rope ladders. As we get to the top, we will quietly knock off the few men on patrol before anyone can sound an alarm."

Hamid started to protest, but Jamil continued dramatically. "Facing the city, I will give the low whistle signal and my hidden Amorites will spring into action. The men on the walls will secure the main tower positions, open the gates, and my Amorite battle cry will be heard on every side."

"No hope! What in the world are we Byblites to do?" muttered Hamid.

But Jamil couldn't be stopped. "Pouring out of your fort, your Byblos soldiers move quickly, even though you are surprised and confused by the sudden attack. But within minutes the unprotected temple areas are under my control. My soldiers are armed with long-bladed bronze daggers and spears, while yours have only copper daggers and axes, and heavy stone maces."

"That's not fair!" Hamid pouted.

"That's right, sweetheart." Jamil loved to mimic gangster movie stars. "By noon, your beautiful city is in flames. The roofs of the temple and palace have all but caved in, and you guys are running around wildly trying to make a fast get-away!"

"Taking my position on the top of the wall, I'll be looking for you, Hamid. Suddenly I see you. But, in a surprise attack, one of your Byblites jumps me from behind and throws me down. But I grab his leg and fling him over the edge of the wall. I then move on to get you, Hamid. You look up, spot me, and begin a battle for your life, for your city."

Valiant Hamid said with spite, "You cruel Amorites have murdered almost everybody, and will force the rest into slavery. Wounded and helpless, I try to hold out."

Jamil still couldn't be stopped "Yeah sweetheart! Wounded, you struggle to defend your people. But by now I control ALL strategic points, even the wall."

"Give me a break," Hamid said sadly. "In one last gallant effort, I cry out to my people, but I am hit by one of your Amorite lances and fall dead."

Dramatically, Hamid threw himself on the ground.

Bossy Jamil triumphantly stood over him and proclaimed, "The battle is over, fatty; won by my Amorites. Byblos has fallen. Along with my lieutenants, I march along the top of the great wall down into the city. After seven hours of combat, your glorious Byblos lies in ruin; most of your men, Hamid, are lost or have fled. the rest of your Byblites fling down their weapons, their strength and courage gone."

Quiet Wasfi interjected, "Those who lived suffered. There was no food, their homes were burned. The civilized, comfortable world they had known was destroyed. Their gods, homes, shipping, fields, their culture — all ruthlessly butchered. I bet the prisoners-of-war were ordered to hard labor. As for the women, they had to care for the sick, and tend to the planting of the scorched fields."

Sammy added, "Jamil's warriors camped in flimsy tents. He permitted no rebuilding. To rebuild would make the city a prize for other invaders."

The closing whistle sounded. 'The gang' managed to shake the battle from their minds. Hamid shivered for a moment, thinking of Byblos' fate, and then began to laugh. Everyone shared in his laughter, not realizing how terribly involved each had been. They all went down to the reefs and spent the rest of the afternoon and that week crabbing and fishing.

But that weekend, Sammy accompanied Clovis on a trip to Beirut to visit the National Museum.

There, Sammy became absolutely fascinated by all the Amorite things, particularly the clay figures of wide-eyed riders on animals' backs, war chariots with four solid wheels, the so-called "Amorite teapot," but he was particularly entranced by their version of the two-headed "push me-pull you." It was just like the one in the Dr. Doolittle story. If nothing else, the Amorites had a sense of humor. Clovis told him that some of those funny figures may have been toys, but others, he thought, had a religious meaning.

It was dark by the time they finally bounced into sleepy Byblos. In front of Nadia's house, Sammy struck out his hand to shake his mentor's.

"Thanks for the trip, Clovis. It was great."

"It was a pleasure, Sammy. See you tomorrow, *bukra*."

They separated, but a moment later glanced back to wave good-bye.

Royal procession to the Temple of the Obelisks led by King Abishemu of Byblos

CHAPTER 6

In The Tomb

Byblos is Rebuilt 2100-1900 and The Middle Bronze Age 1900-1600 B.C.

It was a few days later when Sammy managed to find Clovis alone long enough to ask him whether the beautiful temples were ever rebuilt. The archaeologist replied: "The L-shaped temple was constructed on a completely new plan right on top of the Amorite ash layer." He explained that the three main elements, the outer court, inner court, and sacred room — remained, but now the sacred room was reserved for a large triangular-shaped sandstone obelisk. The inner open courtyard was adorned with more than 29 limestone obelisks ranging from one to more than two meters or three to seven feet high. As they walked through the temple, Sammy was surprised to learn of the changes that had occurred there during the various times of Byblos' occupation. Noting small niches that had been carved in the

center of a few of the sandstone blocks, he asked, "What were those for?"

"They were designed to hold statues of the Canaanite warrior god, Reshef."

"Reshef?" Sammy inquired, "What happened to Baalat Gebal?"

Clovis was delighted to talk about any kind of religion, modern or ancient. He explained that Baalat Gebal continued to be worshipped as the supreme goddess of the city, but now many rituals were related to the god Reshef. "Reshef was the god of war and the son of Baal, the ruler of the gods. We have discovered many figures of him in bronze covered with sheets of beaten gold."

Positioning himself in a striding position, Clovis said: "Reshef stood with one foot forward, fearlessly advancing upon the enemy. Wearing a short, kilt-type skirt and a high conical cap, he held a weapon in his outstretched left hand, perhaps another in his right, and carried a dagger in his belt." The archaeologist looked so funny — he was pretending to be Reshef and posed with one foot forward, his bent left arm held field glasses, the other was raised over his head holding his sun umbrella, and he had put a stick through his belt as a dagger. Sammy laughed because Clovis tried to look fierce, but his eyes were so enormous behind his glasses that it was ridiculous to imagine him as a warrior god! Clovis couldn't look menacing even when he tried.

A few minutes later they stood quietly in the center of the ruined Obelisk Temple. Both archaeologist and boy were lost in thought. Clovis broke the silence by explaining that the temple was not in its original place. "Imagine, archaeologists moved every stone of the temple to this position here so that they could investigate the earlier structures below." He explained to Sammy the problems of moving stone by stone to its new resting place. "Every stone had to be set as it had been originally placed some 4000 years ago."

Sammy was puzzled. "Why did ancient people build in the same place?"

"Perhaps they were superstitious or pious," Clovis said. "If a holy place was destroyed, they often rebuilt another one on top of it. For thousands of years they believed this land to be sacred to the gods."

Clovis thought Sammy's mind might have wandered, so he dramatically positioned himself in front of the temple, and said, "Imagine, Sammy, being transported into the midst of a splendid procession that took place right here. Temple priests following the sacred path which led from the royal palace to the great Temple of Reshef. It is the Festival of Reshef, the God of War, the grandest yearly celebration! This procession stretches out as far as the eye can see. Proud guards on horseback, wearing short kilts, hold ceremonial silver javelins in their outstretched hands. Following are over one-hundred striding warriors with bronze daggers strapped to their waists. As they file past us, the crowd cheers because each family has a son in their ranks. There are splendid foreign envoys, carrying gifts from many lands, who have come to the city especially for the festival. Bearded Ambassadors from Mesopotamia carry ornate bronze weapons, swarthy brown-skinned Arabians bring incense and rare perfumes, and copper vessels full of choice turquoise nuggets are some of the gifts offered by the Sinai delegation. The most spectacular tribute is carried by scarab-ringed Egyptians. They present the most precious gift of all — gold."

"Important, city tradesmen and craftsmen in their best dress follow. Leading them is honored Ipshu, the Chief Architect of the city, the technical genius of temples and tombs, as his father and grandfather had been before him. He wears a cylinder seal around his neck and smiles at the crowd. Ipshu, the engineer, the mason of the majestic Temple of the Obelisks and of the many Obelisks which adorn the courtyard of the Temple of Reshef. Ipshu, the master builder, who builds for the glory of his city."

Finely-dressed members of the royal household come next, but all eyes search for the Crown Prince. Already a man, he, like his father, has a special quality. Someday he will be their ruler and king. Little children throw flowers in his path as he regally strides past. Yes, he is indeed a prince!"

"Then the King's personal guards, selected for their beauty, pass us three abreast. Carrying the royal altar are the religious attendants. Then come teenage youths escorting three enormous black bulls, which meet the approval of the city folk. We all cheer; surely these are the most beautiful animals in the city, fit for sacrifice to the god. After eight tall Nubian standard bearers file by, the King's carrying chair, comes into view. Gold leaf decorations, set in the carved cedar wood chair, gleam in the sunlight."

"Tell me about the King," said Sammy, completely caught up in the story.

"King Abishemu, aged ruler of the Byblites, has governed his people well for many years. He is a wise man, loved and admired by the city folk who cheer wildly and wave flowers as he passes. During the festival of Reshef, he will humble himself to the Warrior God, praying to him to keep the city free from foreign invasion, and to protect his people from harm."

"Wearing a high, rounded, gold crown, just like the warrior god's, the King carries a solid gold decorated axe head. A gold and ivory dagger hangs from his waist. There is little doubt that Byblos is one of the most powerful and richest city-kingdoms of Canaan! Everyone rejoices as the grand procession stops in the outer courtyard of the Temple. The Byblos Navy presents an anchor to the head priests, who bless the group. Once the King is helped down from his chair, the High Priest of Reshef blesses him and his ten warriors, and leads the King through the crowd in the outer court to the open-aired inner courtyard where they both present offerings to the Warrior God. Past victories and vast riches, as well as the safety of the city, are represented by the King's gifts of bronze animals, warrior figurines, weapons, and the King's very own gold, ceremonial axe head."

"At that moment, the sacrificial bulls are led forward. They try to escape, but their struggle is stopped by the priest's hammer. Bellowing in fear they, one by one, are lifted onto the sandstone trough and their throats are slashed. As their blood pours into a lower basin, the people's chanting becomes frenzied. By now a great fire has been built, and the bulls are laid on it. The smoke of the burned sacrifice makes its way into the heavens, and everyone chants their hopes that their sacrifice will please Reshef, their God."

"Great rejoicing follows the presentation of gifts and the prayers. The whole city celebrates, not knowing that soon a sadness will strike."

"Just two days after the Reshef procession, good King Abishemu becomes desperately ill and dies. Clothed in Byblos Canaanite purple, he lies in state in the Palace. A week of mourning is proclaimed, during which time the final arrangements for his enormous stone coffin and his burial are prepared. A special work detail is put into action, headed by the state architect, Ipshu The King's son, and successor to the throne, walks with Ipshu to the sandstone ridge which overlooks the Sea — about one-hundred yards from the Temple of Baalat Gebal. Here they discuss how the enormous limestone coffin, weighing many tons, will be rolled to the vertical tomb passage which workers have cut deep into the living rock from the surface — the depth of a two-storey house with an opening that measures 4 by 4 meters or 13 by 13 feet. Ipshu's men do their work well, and the bottom of the shaft already has a carved horizontal extension. "This makes the whole L-shaped tomb big enough for the large stone coffin to rest at the short end of the "L." Only Ipshu, the trusted architect, knows the secret process for royal burial."

"Ipshu takes his command seriously. Blindfolded workers are led into the tomb and when the blindfolds are removed, they are ordered to fill up the tomb shaft with sand. After that is done, the King's coffin, resting on cedar rollers is pulled onto the top of the fill. When all preparations are completed, a procession of mourners carries the King's royally clad body through the city to his coffin. Everyone cries with grief. They watch and comfort the Crown Prince, the grieving Ipshemuabi. Only a selected few are allowed in the promontory area. The placement of the tomb is to remain a state secret. For the final rites, only family, ministers, and temple priests surround the lifeless body. Fabulous treasures of jewelry, ivory, bronze, silver, gold pendants, weapons, cups, scarabs, and red shiny pottery are buried with the King."

"That night after the mourners return to their homes, slaves, working by torchlight, roll the giant sarcophagus into place and begin to shovel out the earth which fills the shaft. As the earth is taken out from under the logs, the coffin slowly lowers itself down into the shaft. After many hours of hard work, it is rolled into the bottom of the "L", its final place of rest. The shaft is refilled, and stones are carefully placed over its top to hide its secrets from thieves. The whole process has taken two weeks to complete, but now it is done; the King is buried and his resting place is so well-concealed that it will not be discovered for thousands of years."

With a salute Clovis dramatically pronounced: "The King is dead! Long live the King!"

Returning to the present, the two scrambled up the promontory to locate the empty, excavated shaft tomb of King Abishemu. Braving the steep incline of the dark slanting passage leading down into the tomb chamber, Sammy and Clovis carefully inched their way to the burial spot. A little scared, Sammy paused so that his hands could touch the rough sandstone wall. It seemed to take ages to get to the bottom of the "L" where the giant coffin rested in all of its splendor. Sensing that they had had enough of the eerie cool emptiness of the tomb chamber, the two worked their way back up the passage into the sunshine.

Clovis remarked, "Remember the treasures and tomb offerings you saw in the National Museum? Archaeologists discovered these in two groups; some were found inside the King's coffin and others were unearthed under the walls of the Temple of Reshef."

Nothing could have been more exciting than to have found the exquisite dagger of gold, bone and ivory. Sammy sighed. He had actually seen the empty shaft tomb of King Abishemu, the remains of the great temple as well as the treasures which were found in those places. It was almost too hard to believe that they had actually existed!

Later he asked Clovis, "Did Ipshu, the architect, actually exist?"

"Ipshu?" Clovis looked at him and smiled. "Perhaps not, Sammy, but there are many things none of us can ever be really sure of."

But there must have been a master builder of Byblos, he thought to himself. He went off to bed trying to keep his mind on things other than that damp and dark tomb chamber.

Isis brings Osiris back to life with a kiss in the royal palace of Byblos

CHAPTER 7

Isis and Osiris

Late Bronze Age
1600-1200 B.C.

Sunday brought together all the family members to Aunt Nadia's for a splendid dinner. Auntie Huda and other smiling women dressed in traditional sombre black chatted in the living room, busily occupied with their needle work or serving steaming dishes of food to the assembled group. *"tfaddalu!"* said Aunt Nadia cheerily.

"What does that mean?" asked Sammy.

"tfaddalu? It means 'help yourself' in Arabic."

Shish Kebab, tabbouleh, and *kafta* were followed by sweets, lemonade and coffee. The men then retired to long couches conversing in French and Arabic. By now Sammy had heard enough Arabic to understand some of the conversation, and he sat and listened to discussion of the events of the day. His special family favorite, of course, was warm, broad-shouldered, tall Uncle Raymond. For once quiet, Clovis had been included in the dinner party even though he wasn't a real family member.

Naturally he had a special position being an archaeologist who had excavated the ruins for years.

Now that the men had settled down, Sammy found an opportunity to ask Clovis about the strong Egyptian influence in Byblos' history. Clovis settled himself comfortably on the sofa and puffed on his hubbly-bubbly water pipe. When he began to speak, everyone listened. "Egypt and Byblos needed each other, and at different times, one was stronger than the other. They did, however, always solve their differences. Still, their relationship became tricky in the Late Bronze Age. By 1520 B.C.," Clovis continued, "a tribe known as the Hyksos conquered

Egypt using superior methods of warfare, such as the battering ram and the composite bow."

Sammy asked, "What is a composite bow?"

"It was a new weapon for Byblos. Actually, it had been invented earlier, but we find it here in the Late Bronze Age. It was heavier, longer, and stronger than the simple bow. Instead of one simple wooden piece bent by the string, three pieces of wood were fixed together. Now metal-tipped arrows could be shot twice as far, and with much greater accuracy. Late Bronze Age archers used it against the horse and chariot. It was the most effective long range weapon to date. Imagine the archers, Sammy, going into battle. Some were on foot equipped with quivers while others rode in light weight two-wheeled chariots."

Uncle Raymond added, "The soldiers also had coats of mail, shields, spears, swords, and straight long swords. But a most important innovation was the battering ram."

"Please tell me about the battering ram, Clovis," Sammy begged.

"Well, it was a huge war machine that was used to shatter city walls. A wooden pole was hung from a triangular support, and a group of men swung it hard into the weakest point of a wall. After many blows, the wall would be pierced, then collapse and the enemy troops could move in to capture the city."

These facts were interesting, but Uncle Raymond's mind had returned to the Hyksos. "Lets get back to the Hyksos. What happened in Egypt?"

Clovis continued, "Later the Egyptians kicked out the Hyksos, chasing them into areas close to Byblos, where some of them settled."

"Serves them right," Uncle Raymond spoke up. "Did the Hyksos settle right here in Byblos?"

"Yes, but the Egyptian Pharaohs, Thutmoses I and Thutmoses II, again led their armies through Israel, Lebanon and Syria to ensure that the Hyksos would not regroup. Stationing an Egyptian unit in Byblos, they put a local prince, Rib-Addi, in charge: to rule the city and collect taxes."

"What was the next move?" asked Sammy eagerly, making a peace sign.

Clovis shook his head. "No, no peace! Soon another threat came from a northern tribal people known as the *Habiru*, who attacked Byblos time after time and finally gained control. They were followed in 1360 B.C. by the warring *Hittites*. These were yet another conquering people from central Turkey. They forced many cities to become part of their vast Empire but Byblos was taken over by a local leader, Prince Aziru.

"Did the Egyptians do anything about the Hittites?" asked Sammy.

"Hold on! Yes, in 1276 B.C. the Egyptians sent strong armies of the famed Egyptian Pharaoh, Ramses II, to push the Hittites from the area. And, for a while, Byblos and Egypt enjoyed peace."

"*Hamdillila!*" said Uncle Raymond.

Sammy asked Uncle Raymond to tell him about the conquering Philistines, and then to tell a story about Byblos. His Uncle needed little coaxing. He told Sammy that the Philistines were a part of a large tribe known as the "Sea People."

"We are not sure where they came from, but somewhere around 1200 B.C., they invaded, looted, and burned cities in Syria to the north, all along the Canaanite coast, and in Egypt to our south. They were eventually stopped and defeated at the Egyptian border, and were forced to settle down. But ask Clovis about them; he will know more than I do."

Uncle Raymond relaxed in his favorite chair and continued. "Now for the second part of your request — a Byblos story. This story has been passed down to us from one of the greatest of Greek historians, a man named Plutarch. It is a romantic tale and happened a very, very long time ago. It starts in the Egyptian city of Thebes, where there lived a handsome man named Osiris and his beautiful wife, Isis, who helped the poor and the sick. Many years later, Osiris was made King. And while he reigned, there was such peace and plenty throughout Thebes that he was called to be King — or Pharaoh — of all Egypt. Osiris was a wise and kind ruler who was loved by his people."

"And then?" asked Sammy.

Uncle Raymond went on. "But there was an evil man who was jealous of Osiris: his ugly brother, Seth. Seth was as evil as Osiris was good. Osiris was kind even to him, but unhappiness, fighting, and drinking followed wherever Seth went. Tricky Seth schemed to murder Osiris so that he could become king of Egypt himself."

"So he played a dirty trick?" Sammy asked.

Uncle Raymond nodded. "Now the intrigue begins! One day Seth visited Osiris, offering to make him a beautiful garment. Osiris was measured, and some time later Seth presented him with a truly marvelous robe. He then persuaded Osiris to be his guest at a banquet. Isis was suspicious of Seth's motives and begged her husband to stay at home, but Osiris felt that he must attend the feast."

"The evening was very spirited. After dinner, Seth's servants carried a richly decorated, large golden box into the banquet hall. Seth announced

55

that he would present the form-fitting box to any one who could lie down in it. One by one the guests, desirous of the box, tried it out, but nobody's body fit properly. Then it was Osiris' turn. To everyone's amazement, Osiris fit into the box perfectly! Then all at once, before any of the guests knew what was happening, Seth slammed the lid shut. His soldiers picked up the box, ran to the river, and heaved it into the fast-flowing Nile!"

"Osiris was in trouble! How could he breathe? Did he die? Is that the end of the story?" Sammy asked.

"Not yet," answered Uncle Raymond. "When Isis was told of her husband's fate, she was heart-broken and searched along the Nile for his body. One evening, as she was looking for her loved one, she came upon the god Pan, who felt sorry for her. He told Isis that the box with her husband's body had floated into the Mediterranean Sea and then north to Byblos. He had heard that the box had been engulfed by a giant tamarisk tree there. The King of Byblos had the large tree cut down and made it into the center pillar of his palace."

"But couldn't he see the box was there?"

"No, he didn't know that the box lay within the heart of the tree." After lighting a cigar, Uncle Raymond said, "Don't forget, this is a legend, and the truth, if there is any, is exaggerated."

"Did Isis travel to Byblos?" asked Sammy.

"Yes, and once there, she had to find her way into the Palace. Daily, she visited the fresh-water spring where the Queen's hand-maidens came to draw water and gossip. She discovered the King had gone on a hunting trip, and the Queen was alone caring for their sick infant son. As a matter of fact, the Queen was desperate — the baby would not stop crying. Isis made it known to the hand-maidens that she could cure the baby Prince. This news was carried to the Queen who asked to see Isis. And so Isis gained entrance to the palace, and was such a good nurse that the baby stopped crying. Before the King returned, Isis had gained royal favor because she had restored health to the baby Prince."

"The King was so grateful to find his son well again that he granted Isis any thing she desired. Naturally, she wanted the great, central pillar of the Palace. Although amazed by her request, the King had the pillar cut down and the beautiful box was dug out of its heart. When the box was opened before an amazed group of palace courtiers, Isis brought Osiris back to life with a kiss of love. Before returning to Egypt, Isis and Osiris revealed their identity and blessed the King of Byblos and his city."

"And when they arrived in Egypt?" asked Sammy.

"They defeated cruel Seth, who had all but destroyed the land while he ruled. Isis and Osiris worked hard to bring their country back to the great happiness and prosperity it had known before." Uncle Raymond drew a deep breath. "So ends one of the legends of Isis and Osiris. There are many more tales that were built up around their goodness."

"That's a great story Uncle. Thanks, I really enjoyed it!"

Uncle Raymond went to change into his old clothes and left Sammy thinking about how fond he was of his new-found family. Between Clovis and Uncle Raymond, they seemed to know everything there was to know about history and legends. Sammy loved to learn all the wonderful things they knew, and felt very lucky to be with them.

58

Wenamon in the port of Byblos patiently awaits to be received by Zakar-Baal

CHAPTER 8   A Phoenician Ship

The Iron Age
1200-539 B.C.

A Phoenician ship! Sammy was speechless with delight. It was now more than a month that Sammy was in Byblos, and last night after dinner, Uncle Raymond had presented him with a large, wooden model of a Phoenician galley, complete with a lion-headed prow and three masts with squared-off sails. There were two decks below with a crew made up of forty oarsmen, twenty on each side. Shielded soldiers protected the flanks. "This is an exact replica of the type of ship which carried Phoenicians across the seas to set up trading posts and colonial cities throughout the Mediterranean," said Uncle Raymond. Sammy asked to hear more about his illustrious ancestors, the famous Phoenicians.

"The word *Phoenician* was bestowed on us by the Greeks," said Clovis opening an atlas he was holding. "Knowledge of the trade routes and Mediterranean ports made them 'Masters of the Sea'. Look here on this map. They founded such large modern cities as Marseilles in France, Cadiz in Spain, and Carthage, modern Tunis, in Tunisia. For archaeologists, the name Phoenician applies only to the so-called Iron Age, or to the period between 1200 and 539 B.C."

Sammy examined his ship. Noticing its name written in a strange script, he exclaimed, "Is this written in ancient Phoenician?"

"Yes, it is. The greatest Phoenician contribution to civilization was their carrying of the 22-letter alphabet to the far reaches of their trading world as early as the 8th Century B.C. We use most of those letters in our alphabet today. Just think - Greek,

Latin, Arabic, Hebrew, Russian, Sanskrit, even Korean — most of the writing of the world has come from Phoenician."

On the next evening, cradling his boat model in his arms, Sammy made his way down to the horseshoe shaped port. He propped himself up on the breakwater and watched his trim little galley ride the waves. Looking around in the nearly deserted inner harbor, he saw half a dozen stumpy fishing boats tied up to the cement quay; the rest had gone out for the evening catch. Now the beacons began to reflect brightly on the water. The half-ruined Crusader towers stood high by the entrance to the inner harbor and were reflected in the water. Behind him, fishermen hung their nets to dry. One of Raymond's friends was mending a net in the light of a kerosene lantern. Battered rubber buckets, some ropes and canvas lay about. Filling the air were the strains of a lovely Arabic song from Pepé's Fishing Club restaurant.

Sammy fixed his eyes on a small cluster of stars so far away that he could see them clearly only when he squinted. He wondered if anyone else in the whole world had ever looked at those tiny specks. Maybe a Phoenician. The puttering of the motor from Uncle Raymond's boat brought him abruptly back to the present.

"Hey there!" he heard his uncle's voice call cheerfully from a distance. "The catch was excellent. Come and give me a hand with it."

Sammy reached the end of the pier in time to help his uncle steady the boat as it docked. As he helped lug the catch and tackle, Sammy updated Uncle Raymond and told him about the seaworthiness of his Phoenician boat. Uncle Raymond's fishing had been very good; lots of red mullet, a few squid, shrimp, and Mediterranean dorade. Sammy learned how to divide the fish for weighing, how to stow the gear, and to string up the nets to dry in the night air. After this was all done, he grew impatient.

"Another story. Please, Uncle."

Uncle Raymond laughed, then quietly put his arm around Sammy and led him to the remains of a Roman column base on which they sat. "Whoa — be patient Sammy! You should have a bit of background before you can understand the stories of the Iron Age. As you've probably guessed, in the Iron Age the art of working iron had become widespread. It was not that much stronger or more durable than bronze, but its low price and large supply put iron tools into the hands of everyone. Most ships bound for Byblos were a lure to pirates because they carried precious cargoes of gold and silver, both to buy cedar wood and to use as gifts for the king. The mighty Egyptian empire was beginning to crumble in about 1100 B.C., and Byblos was able to stand up for herself."

"Uncle, can we get to the story? I hope it's about pirates!"

"Well, it is, Sammy, to some extent. But it is also about the power play between Egypt and Byblos at that time."

"Great!" Sammy said, making himself comfortable.

"This is probably a true story, Sammy. It was found in Egypt, written on a 3000-year-old papyrus. The pharaoh of Egypt wanted to build a sacred boat of Byblos cedar for Amon-Ra, the most important god in Egypt. Unfortunately, Egypt had fallen on hard times and was so disorganized that it could not produce enough money, or even its own ship to make the voyage to Byblos. However, Wenamon, an official of the temple of Amon in Thebes, set sail for Byblos on the 16th day of the 4th month of the 3rd season in the 5th year of Ramses' reign."

"Is that what the papyrus says?" asked Sammy.

"Exactly. And we know that Wenamon carried some gold and over three kilos (six pounds) of silver, in partial payment for the cedar. He also carried a traveller's statue of the god, Amon-Ra, a sort of 'Amon-of-the-Road,' which he hoped Prince Zakar-Baal of Byblos would accept as the balance of the payment. Along the way, at Dor, at that time a Philistine city, he was robbed of everything but the statue. After nine days and with little hope, Wenamon decided to take justice into his own hands and made off with some Philistine silver, hid it in the statue, found a ship going north, and fled."

"Once in the harbor, Wenamon must have seen the rich, powerful galleys of Phoenician Byblos, for this was a period that marked the beginning of the Golden Age of Phoenician power. He petitioned Byblos' Prince for help. The Prince was suspicious of Wenamon because he had no money as tribute — he was empty-handed, except, of course, for the statue. He had brought neither the usual gifts nor any proof of his identity. So the Prince refused to listen to the Egyptian's request."

"What did he do then?"

"The Prince snubbed Wenamon and made him camp out on this very beach. He wouldn't even receive him. Every day for twenty-nine days, he sent him a message saying, 'Get out of my harbor!' Wenamon was frantic. He tried to find a way home to Egypt, but just as he found passage on a ship, the Prince changed his mind and ordered him to stay!"

"But why couldn't he make up his mind?" This was difficult for Sammy to understand.

61

"Well, we don't know for sure, but perhaps there had been a cut-back in the lumber business, or Egypt and her gods may have still had some clout. It seems that the Prince's son was ill, and perhaps he thought the power of the Egyptian 'Amon-of the-Road' might help."

"Anyway, what happened then?"

"The next morning, the Prince, Zakar-Baal, sent for Wenamon and said, 'Where is your gold and your silver?' Wenamon was upset when the Prince said to him that if his story of the loss of his gifts were true, his weak country, Egypt, had obviously supplied him with a second-rate ship, a second-rate Captain, and most important of all, without enough protection from pirates. Therefore his mission was doomed from the beginning. Poor helpless Wenamon was caught in the politics of his day. He was desperate."

"Uncle, what could Wenamon say?"

"We actually know the conversation. It was written by Wenamon, or one of his scribes. He wrote, 'I was silent.' Then Zakar-Baal knowingly asked, 'On what business have you come?'."

"I have come for cedar! Your father sold it to us, and his father before him, and you will do it too!"

"The Prince answered, 'To be sure they did. And if you give me something for it, I will, too. In those days, the Pharaoh would send six ships loaded with Egyption goods: papyrus, gold, fine linens, alabaster, and turquoise. You bring me nothing!'"

"He then summoned the scribes to bring out past records, and read aloud to Wenamon that the Egyptians had traditionally paid great amounts of tribute in silver and fine goods, in addition to important personal gifts for the King. The Prince continued to drive a hard bargain. 'You bring no royal gifts. If you had gold or silver, I would cry out and the heavens would open! Logs would roll down and lie upon the shore. Why have you made this foolish trip?'"

"Wenamon replied, 'This is no silly trip! Amon is the God of Egypt — the God of all lands. The sea is his, and the Lebanon is his, and yet you have made this great god wait twenty-nine days moored in your harbor. You are here to carry on commerce of the Lebanon with Amon, its lord! Amon was the Lord of your fathers — when Egypt held sway over Byblos, Egypt's chief god would have ruled here too — and you also are the servant of Amon!'"

"Zakar-Baal then relented, 'If you say to Amon — I will do it, I will carry out the commission, then you will be prosperous, healthy, and good to your land and your people!'"

"That sounds like a god-bribe!" said Sammy.

"So, Prince Zakar-Baal compromised," said Uncle Raymond. "He had a ship's keel, a bow-post, a stern-post, plus four other hewn logs sent to Egypt. And in return, the officers of Amon in Egypt sent him a shipload of goods: royal linens, gold, silver, cowhides, lentils, and fish. This pleased the Prince. He detailed 300 men, plus supervisors, and 300 oxen, to cut down and drag the cedar to the port."

"Said Zakar-Baal, 'See what my fathers have done, I have done also, even though you have not done for me what your father would have done. The last of your wood lies here. Load it in. And don't look at the sea. Don't look at the wind or waves as an excuse for delay!'"

"So all is well that ends well, *hamdilla*," said Sammy, using his new word of Arabic.

Sammy's uncle patted him on the back. "Wenamon had no one to protect him. In those days people were very suspicious of a man without official papers, and certainly suspicious of a merchant without gold. You see, people didn't journey then as they do today."

Sammy thought to himself that people today without passports or identification could be in big trouble, too.

"His personal report to the Pharaoh was uncovered in Egypt by archaeologists," said Uncle Raymond. "It showed us that the Phoenicians had organized groups of trading ships, which sailed under the control of local princes. These princes provided money for the building of fleets, offered protection from pirates, and, naturally, shared in the profits. Poor Wenamon was caught without this protection. What I'm getting at, Sammy, is that by Wenamon's time, the Phoenician cities of Byblos,

Sidon, and Tyre were as strong as Egypt. Maybe the King of Byblos wanted to get some revenge too — an international 'eye for an eye.'"

Sensing that the boy was troubled over this long-ago tragedy, Uncle Raymond suggested they meet Clovis in the café for an evening snack instead of going right home.

Sammy felt a little better after a *kibbé*, a tasty dish of spiced, minced lamb. Then he lingered with the men and asked them to explain things, such as the importance of King Ahiram's tomb, the tomb of the Iron Age Phoenician King. "Okay, so why is it important?" he asked.

"Well, Sammy," said Uncle Raymond, "the *sarcophagus*, the limestone coffin the king is buried in, has an inscription on its side that we think is the oldest example of Phoenician writing ever discovered. It dates perhaps to the 11th-10th centuries B.C.! And where did this remarkable find occur? In Byblos!"

"Wow! That is something! What does it say?"

Clovis then took over. "It reads, 'The son of Ahiram, King of Byblos, commissioned this sarcophagus for his father as his eternal home. If any King or Commander attacks Byblos and brings this coffin to light, let him live a broken man and let peace leave Byblos, and let a hoodlum ruin his inscriptions!'"

Because Tewfik wanted to close the coffee house for the night, Clovis proposed they walk over

to the site and inspect the tomb by moonlight. Weary Uncle Raymond decided to return home. Supplied with flashlights, Sammy and Clovis scrambled up to one of the highest points on the rocky ridge. The now empty shaft tomb looked even more mysterious in the light of the moon. Clovis shone his light on the tomb's walls until it rested midway down the shaft.

"This is just like a Middle Bronze Age shaft tomb that I climbed down into the other day," said Sammy, feeling a shiver travel up and down his spine.

"Yes," said Clovis. "Some scholars think this shaft may also date back to the Middle Bronze period, and was simply re-used in the Iron Age. Now, look over there, where the light rests. The King's sarcophagus may be in the National Museum in Beirut, but I can show you another alphabetic inscription that some of us think dates just as early, and was probably done at the same time. See it? Carved onto the wall."

The boy's eyes picked out what he knew were Phoenician letters.

"The inscription reads," Clovis chanted in a deep eerie voice. 'WARNING HERE! YOUR DEATH IS BELOW!'"

"Creepy!" exclaimed Sammy, anxiously gazing down. He could smell history.

"This, of course, was to discourage any tomb robbers who were after the treasures buried with the king."

Sammy sighed. "So no robbers broke into this tomb?"

"Unfortunately, Sammy, yes, they did. There were thieves around in those days too, for the tomb was robbed in antiquity." Clovis was waving the flashlight in the air. "Ancient robbers were usually able to find the secret entrance and would steal everything!"

"And as far as modern robbers are concerned," said Sammy, "their looting also destroys contexts — as if the coffin was taken out of the tomb. That puts the limelight on the object, the coffin in this case, not on its environment — the tomb — or on the culture or idea that made it, right?"

"What a young archaeologist!" said Clovis triumphantly.

Sammy and Clovis walked slowly home. Both were quiet, absorbed in their own thoughts. Sammy now felt, more than ever that these tombs, hid some secret. Each had its own space — its own time of glory — the things that made it live, and its own end. He wished he could understand the whole truth of these things.

Sarcophagus of King Ahiram in Beirut National Museum

65

Clovis excavates around the Persian platform and fortress with Sammy looking on

CHAPTER 9

Sebastian

Byblos under Persian Rule
539-332 B.C.

By now, Sammy felt at ease among the ruins and could explore areas out of the way of guided tours. The area was small enough to become familiar ground and he had a passing knowledge of almost every structure and its history. One of his favorite spots was near the Persian fortress, where Clovis was excavating. From a distance, the boy would watch the careful exploration of the earth, hoping to be on the spot when new finds appeared and the clues were put together.

When there was a break, Sammy would enjoy talking to Clovis about people of the past; what they built, how they worshipped, fought wars, travelled and traded. He tried to understand the spirit, ideas and way of life of those who had lived in Byblos long ago. At some other times he would

make a sketch, but almost always he tore it up. Often he would think, "How do you draw ruins? It seems impossible to draw every single element — every building has its own meaning. How can I make each period, even each structure, into a living whole? If I could only see the oneness of a period, its atmosphere, its details." He knew he had begun to identify with Byblos and with its riddles, just as an archaeologist does.

Then his attention was drawn to the excavations. Two men were bending over plans. Their backs were turned to Sammy, but he recognized one of them to be the eminent French archaeologist, Maurice Dunand. He was a much older man, and wore a French beret and faded khaki pants. He was known as the father of Byblos archaeology, and had been excavating the site since the 1920s. His team, including Clovis, was now working in the later periods , the empires, beginning with the Persians, followed by the Greeks, and then the Romans.

Sammy decided to explore the Persian area for himself. Leisurely climbing onto a newly excavated wall, he walked along it and decided to take a look.

"Stop! Stop! Stop!" Clovis gave out a quick cry of alarm. "Sammy, get off that wall. Quick!"

The boy took a step backwards and knocked down a large stone and earth which fell into the trench.

Clovis bounded over to the wall. When Sammy regained his balance and looked at him, he saw only anger on Clovis' face. "Shame on you," said Clovis, shaking his head. "Now you're creating havoc. You are polluting the site. Never, never, never, walk on a wall. Look what you've done! You have destroyed it." He waved his trowel in Sammy's face and continued. "The fallen stones have to be put back in position along with the earth or else they can't be plotted. If they are left where they have fallen, they will confuse the excavation of the next level. What a mess you've made! The stones and earth will never rest as they were originally placed. Oh, I can't believe it, I am so angry! I thought you were intelligent."

Sammy had listened to Clovis without uttering a word. He hardly dared to breathe.

"I can't let you near the excavation if you're going to do stupid things like this. Go away, go do something. Fish or swim with 'the gang'. Get out of my hair. Go away now. Get lost, *yellah!*"

"I'm so sorry," was all Sammy could say. Horrified at the consequences of his actions, he quickly moved out of sight over to the Persian period platform. And he walked slowly out of the excavation area. Then he heard a low whimpering noise. Sounds like an animal in trouble, he thought. Heading toward the sound, he heard it again! Suddenly he saw a great, hairy, black and white mound with two bright eyes peering out at him through a fringe of hair.

"Take it easy, I'm coming," Sammy called. He could see that it was a big shaggy dog, with an injured right paw held at an awkward angle. Panting in pain, the animal wagged his tail at having company.

"Oh, poor dog." Sammy patted him gently. "Don't worry, I'll take care of you. If Clovis finds you here, he'll think I brought you inside and really nail me to the wall."

Thus Sammy found a new friend with whom to explore the ruins. He named the big stray mongrel 'Sebastian'. With time and care the foot healed, and he and Sammy spent hours with 'the gang' finding new ways to sneak in and around the ancient city. Clovis was no longer angry and did not seem to mind Sammy's hairy friend — or, at least, pretended

68

that he didn't. Sammy was happy that he and Clovis were good friends again.

One day the two returned to the area of the new dig. Sculpted into the side of the huge Persian stone platform was a friendly-looking lion's head. Sebastian barked a greeting, but, receiving no acknowledgement, stalked off. Laughing, Sammy whistled him to come back and the two pals trotted off to seek an explanation from Clovis of such an enormous structure .

"What is that?" asked the budding archaeologist.

"The block carved with the lion's head and paws was a part of a Persian platform. But," Clovis continued, "little remains of the mighty building because the Greeks re-used the Persian stones in their own constructions. That's why stones can be quite a puzzle to sort out. I'll show you what I mean." Clovis explained that different types of stones were used in different periods, and that each period could be recognized by the way the stones were dressed.

Sammy giggled, "A dressed stone? Come on, Clovis, stop joking!"

"No, it's true, Sammy. I know it sounds strange, but it means the way the stone is cut. See here, for instance. These huge, two-to-six ton blocks, with their centers sticking out, indicate Persian building stones. The stones had been deliberately quarried for their size and dressed — or decorated — with

bulging centers in this way. When we find such a block used in a later building, it means, of course, that later people reused it. Even today, in modern Byblos homes, many of the stones are ancient. People found them lying around and just decided it was easier to build with them instead of bothering to buy or cut new stones."

Sammy groaned. "What guesswork archaeology can be!"

Clovis said, "Not always! That's why it's so exciting! It's a living science!"

Sebastian was sniffing at Sammy's sandwich bag. The next second he grabbed it and made a dash for his hiding place. He was still limping, so he didn't get very far. Sammy caught up with him, and guilty Sebastian, looking very meek, dropped the bag and stood half-wagging his tail. Clovis was laughing.

"Clovis, what happened in the Persian period?" asked Sammy.

"Well, for fun, let's pretend that you are the Persian military Governor of the *Satrapy*, or province of a large region, that included Byblos. If you were a teenager you might have marched with the brilliant General-King Cyrus II, known as Cyrus the Great. Imagine, Cyrus made conquests that extended from the Hellespont in Greece to the frontiers of India. After he died in 529 B.C., his power passed to Cambyses, and then to the brilliant administrator, Darius I, who ruled from 522 to 486. Darius divided the empire into twenty provinces known as satrapies. So, as Governor or Satrap of the province that included Byblos, you carry out the wise policy of Persian officials by allowing the city to maintain its own king, to speak its own Semitic language, and to worship gods of its own choosing — and you encourage it to trade throughout the Mediterranean world. You are responsible only to the Persian King. Your friend, Byblos' King Yehowmilk, is a good and sensible man who devotes his time to civic duties. The two of you would share a common interest in the new idea of using coins for business, and both of you take special pride in the city's right to mint its own coins."

"The art of striking coins was a marvelous innovation in the way people traded. Instead of exchanging goods, they now had a system of uniform weights and measures and used coins as money. Only the King could strike gold coins, the *daric*, worth then about $10.00. But the satraps were allowed to strike their own silver and bronze coins, for the gold to silver ratio was about 13 to 1. The Byblites had the honor of the Persian King's official certification to mint their own silver *staters*, as the coins were known. The one Persian demand was that the design on the coins was to portray the city's greatness."

"Everyone would be excited about the design competition and every craftsman would be busy working on ideas. At that time Greek pottery was being imported to Byblos and inspired everyone. City potters were now painting their pots with stories taken from Greek mythology. At that time too, a group of Byblites were serving in the Persian Navy; they fought in the Battle of Miletus of 494 B.C. against the Greeks.

"You, Sammy, as the Satrap, would join with the King to judge the competition. Eventually that day would come, and a great procession would make its way through the city up the sculpted stairway to the magnificent podium reserved for state and festive occasions. King Yehowmilk, wearing the cylindrical headdress of Kingship and a rich royal purple cloak over a long tunic, would address the people of Byblos this way.

"In the traditions of our forefathers, the coin of our city has been designed with a Phoenician ship whose prow ends in a lion's head. Inside the galley there are three crest-helmeted soldiers carrying the round shields of the city. Below the ship is a seahorse, representing our command over the sea. All of this is enclosed in a border of dots. On the back of the coin is a vulture standing on a ram within a dotted border. These traditions are a part of Byblos; our city applauds these ideas, and the King and the Governor congratulate our master designer. Come forward!"

"With that, you, the Satrap, would decorate the winner with a ribbon on which hangs a gold daric, the coin of Persia. Great festivities would then follow."

Sebastian was licking Sammy's hand. He scratched the dog's tummy and the ruff behind his ears. Picking up his papers, Clovis saluted the two, and said that he must return to work. Suddenly Sebastian took off towards the promontory chasing a stray cat. Knowing there might be trouble, Sammy jumped up and ran in hot pursuit. Something was strange about the site. He realized what it was: all the workers had gone home. It was deserted. Foolish Sebastian was nowhere to be seen. He sat and waited and then decided to walk to the promontory. As he passed the tomb area, he heard a series of dull, unmistakable sounds. Someone was digging. Edging his head over the precipice, he saw the figure of a massive man, apparently so absorbed in his work that he did not notice Sammy and he kept on hacking away at the earth. What was odd was that he was dressed in a guard's uniform. Sammy knew all of the guards; this man was an unknown, and

working well beyond the view of the guards.

Sammy stood for a moment, rigid, trying to decide what to do. But then he caught sight of Sebastian who in turn had spied him, barked, and was run-limping straight for him. The man heard the dog and raised his eyes to Sammy. He said, "Damn, it's you, the one who knows how to keep a secret!"

Sammy shuddered. He remembered, feared and hated that voice. It was the voice of his first night in Byblos. He had dreamt about that horrible night, but knew that this was no dream.

"What are you standing there for? Come down here with me!" And with a rough laugh he continued, "Come down, nice little boy, I want to show you what I've found."

"He must think that I'm a fool," Sammy thought.

When he smiled, Sammy noticed a large mole on his chin. Realizing that Sammy was not going to move, the man's strong mouth hardened. "It is too bad for you that you have seen me."

Sammy's heart was beating fast and he didn't know what to do. He stared silently back at the man who, meanwhile, was rapidly making his way up the cliff towards him. Without waiting, Sammy took to his heels, and instinctively retreated as fast as he could. Sebastian had never seen his master move so quickly. The next moment both swept into Tewfik's. With a quick glance he found Clovis. "Come, quickly!" he shouted breathlessly. "Someone is

71

digging on the promontory near the tombs. It must be a thief!"

"Curses!" roared Clovis, jumping up. "Quick! Come!"

Everyone jumped up and frantically rushed to the spot, but it was too late. A gaping hole in the earth was all there was left to see. The robber had gone and there was no sign of him. During the late afternoon and well into the evening a search was conducted, but the thief's escape had succeeded. Sammy had to report to the police, who told him excitedly that looting had become more frequent and daring. Thieves even used dynamite to break open unprotected sites.

Clovis, moving his hands to emphasize his words, was furious. "Thugs! This is war! They are destroying Byblos and we are being betrayed! We must be merciless!"

That very evening a citizen guard patrol was established.

Followed by Sebastian, who was doing a good job keeping up with his master, Sammy rushed home hoping he would be the first to tell his Aunt Nadia what happened. But news travels fast in a small town. She was comforting, but noticeably worried, and when she worried, the furrow lines in her forehead became accentuated. In minutes Uncle Raymond rushed into the house. Aunt Nadia quietly told him that she felt that Sammy was in danger.

Later Clovis came for a visit and brought Sammy a copy of a Persian period coin. It felt so heavy in his hand. How thick it was! Yes, and there was the ship, the soldiers, even the sea horse. "Did the Persians win all of their sea battles against the Greeks?" he asked.

"No. At the Battle of Marathon in 490 B.C., the great Persian sea power crumbled against a much smaller Greek fleet, but superior Greek strategy! For some time, the world of Byblos, however, remained essentially Persian in perspective. Because the Persians showed tolerance to those they ruled, the Byblites continued to govern themselves. And then about 150 years later, Alexander the Great came to this city which surrendered without a struggle, as did many others throughout the Eastern Mediterranean. Alexander's arrival ended the Persian period everywhere he went."

"Tell me, Clovis, how do you feel about the site? About, for example, the Persian platform you are working on, or the ruins in general."

"Are you serious, Sammy?"

"Yes." Sammy noticed a wistful far-off look as Clovis replied.

"Each building contains all the mystery of the men who built it and the people who lived, worshipped or fought for it. The mask is its stones and its design. Sometimes it is impossible for me to imagine how a particular building served people long ago. Many times I look endlessly at a structure, I almost have a love affair with it. I want to understand everything about it, its purpose, its relationship to other structures, and finally and most important of all, its meaning and significance to the men, women and children who used it. I want to see into the very *ethos* or spirit of its existence."

Their conversation then returned to the incident. Sammy recounted his story of his first night's secret adventure to Clovis. The door was partially open. Aunt Nadia entered the room, and gave strict instructions to both of them to always stay together when Sammy was on the site. Sammy was annoyed. The freedom that had been given to him was now being taken away.

The Greek theater of Byblos and *palaestra* with athletes practicing their skills

CHAPTER 10

The Olympics

Hellenistic Byblos
332-64 B.C.

Everyone was crowded around Tewfik's television — it was just about the largest one in the old town — watching a special program dedicated to the Olympics. The whole world was anticipating the Games. Sammy was intrigued; it was the first time he'd ever paid much attention to them.

At the end of the program, he looked inquiringly at Clovis whose brown eyes were alive with interest, "You know, Sammy, the Olympic Games were the greatest festival of athletic competition in Ancient Greece."

"How did they decide to call them 'Olympic Games'?"

Clovis explained that the games were under the patronage of the father and ruler of the Greek gods, Zeus. "They were held during the summer once every four years at the sacred sanctuary of Olympia, not to be confused, my boy, with the *home* of the gods, Mt. Olympos in northern Greece! In those times, only twenty-four contests were held. The most important were the foot races, wrestling, the pentathlon, boxing, horse races and, grandest of all, chariot races."

"Could everyone take part, that is, if they were good enough?"

"Glad you asked. No. Only men participated. Not only were no women allowed to compete, they weren't even allowed to watch!"

"No Women's Lib then, huh?" Sammy remarked. "Did the winners receive gold medals as they do today?"

"Oh, no. The winners were only crowned with

olive branches. But anyone receiving this honor, as well as the Greek state or province that they came from, was more proud of this athletic victory than even winning battles!"

"Amazing! Did Byblos ever compete in the Games?"

"We don't know, Sammy. The Games were very Greek in spirit and only those who could speak Greek could participate. However, during the Hellenistic period, Greek was the *lingua franca*, the common language, which was spoken even in Byblos. I'm sure that Byblos athletes at least trained for the Olympic events, because it was a part of the Greek influence brought here by Alexander the Great in 332 B.C."

Everyone lingered in the café to watch the late news on television. Soon after, Sebastian walked Sammy home. After settling the dog in his new basket, the boy went to his room and got ready for bed. When all was quiet, Sebastian pushed open the bedroom door and jumped on to Sammy's bed.

The next morning when Sammy awoke, he overheard a spirited conversation going on in the living room. Aunt Nadia was very upset, and he could tell she was talking about Sebastian. In a few minutes, she burst into his room, looked him straight in the eye, and said in her best English, "Bad boy! Bad dog! No dog on bed in my house! *Mish quoise*! I throw outside dog!"

"But you don't understand, Auntie, Sebastian has no other friends but me. He just wants to be a person — like me!"

His aunt's eyes were flashing. "No dog on bed! I have put up with your collections of *whatever* spread all across this house but I will not allow that dog to sleep on your bed!" And with that she angrily went into the kitchen.

Sammy was worried. Sebastian was gone. He must have known that the heated discussion was about him, but suppose he was lost? Sammy didn't take time for breakfast but quickly threw on his jeans and dashed off to search for his friend.

"Sebastian! Come here! Where are you?" An anxious Sammy snapped his fingers and whistled for his four-legged friend. A black shaggy head peered over the outer wall of the Crusader fortress and saw Sammy walking toward him. He gave a loud bark for attention, then bounded down into the ruins. Sammy laughed and followed in running leaps.

It was a great hide-and-go-seek game they played in and out of the ancient castle, down the

Crusader period ramp, over to the dark tombs of the Middle Bronze Age, and down to the port and back.

After a long morning, Sammy wanted to find Clovis to hear all about Alexander the Great's conquest of Byblos. Sebastian had other ideas; he wanted to play some more. Later, panting with exhaustion, boy and dog collapsed on a patch of soft grass and within minutes Sebastian was all but asleep, with one eye closed and the other fighting to keep on the alert should his master have any more fun ideas.

With a sandwich in hand for Sammy, Clovis found them. As they ate, Clovis knew exactly what Sammy wanted to hear, a story about Hellenistic Byblos and something about his favorite hero, Alexander the Great.

"After Alexander and his Macedonian warriors had peacefully 'conquered' Byblos the process of Hellenization began. Splendid Greek temples and stately private homes, were built according to Alexander's plans. In this process, much of the physical remains of earlier periods were razed, and earlier occupation levels were destroyed. Byblos now looked like an entirely Greek city. Much of her earlier Phoenician identity was lost."

"But how did the city look? Can we imagine it?" asked Sammy.

"Sure, we can try. If we visited Hellenistic Byblos, one stop would have been at gym, known then as the *palaestra*. Here men were wrestling,

throwing the javelin or discus, while others were boxing, and still others were running in track competitions. All of these events were part of Olympic athletic training.

"After passing through the busy market place, known in Greek as the *agora*, we would have come to a white marble theater glistening in the sun. We would climb to the top of the tiers of stone seats, which had been built into the hillside to form a semi-circular auditorium. We would have noted that the front rows were reserved for the city dignitaries, and that there was a two-story stage area which supported columns for the scenery. This was a typical Hellenistic theater, more sophisticated than the earlier Classical Greek ones where the actors performed and the *chorus* intoned in the round *orchestra* center of the perfectly circular theater. The acoustics were so perfect that even the quietist whispers of the actors could be heard in every seat of this superbly designed structure.

"We might have seen a rehearsal of the Greek play, *Medea* by Euripides. As was the custom, the lead role would be played by a man wearing a woman's mask. Women were never allowed to appear on the stage."

"Clovis, didn't you once tell me that 'Byblos' is a Greek word?"

"Yes, Sammy. It was the Greeks who named the city, which in their ancient language meant the Egyptian word, *papyrus*. From its name we have inherited the words bible, bibliography, and many others. Papyrus is a grasslike plant which could be sliced, pressed, and dried into a kind of writing paper. It was used long before man invented paper. Papyrus did not come to the Greeks directly, but was instead exported from Egypt to Byblos, and then in turn exported to the Greeks. You might call Byblos the 'middle man'."

Just as Clovis was finishing his explanation, Sebastian found a stick. He proudly presented it to his master, begging him to throw it. Sammy threw it further and further to please his furry friend. He threw the stick until his arm ached. Clovis laughed. Then they all headed for Aunt Nadia's.

"Hi, I'm back!" announced Sammy standing at the top of the stairs.

"Well, I'm certainly relieved," said Aunt Nadia smiling.

When Aunt Nadia saw Sammy with Sebastian, she admitted the shaggy stray into the house. As she held the door open for the two, she firmly said, "Not on bed!" As they both passed by her, she winked at him.

Sammy went to Nadia and said, "You are the most wonderful Auntie in the world!" He hugged her, "Thanks!"

After dinner, Clovis gave Sammy the *Iliad*, the story of the Trojan War. "It was written by Homer, the greatest of all of the Greek story tellers. He wrote it about a war between the Greeks and

Trojans that happened long before his own time."

Sammy took it to bed with him. The Greek heroes, Achilles, Agamemnon, Ajax, Odysseus, all seemed to come alive through their troubles during their long siege of Troy. The Trojan hero, Hector, and his brother Paris, who had started the whole war ten years before by kidnapping the beautiful Helen, wife of the King of Sparta, also sprung to life as he read. Oh, and the Trojan Horse, it was fantastic. He couldn't put the book down. He spent the next four days on his balcony, reading, with Sebastian curled up at his feet. He read and dreamed about these great heroes, just as many had done in Hellenistic Byblos.

The colonnade and *nympheum* of Roman Byblos

CHAPTER 11

Astarte and Adonis

Roman Byblos
64 B.C.-330 A.D.

After breakfast the next morning, Sammy met Uncle Raymond in the *souk* who suggested that he might like to visit the old family mansion which stood back in the hills a kilometer or so from Byblos. "It's a charming old place where the family retreats when the humidity becomes unbearable." Uncle Raymond said.

"Oh, yes," Sammy agreed, "I'd love to!"

A winding road with hairpin curves led to a 100-year-old house with arched windows built overlooking the rocky coast. From the terrace, Byblos could be seen below, its two harbors framing the spit of land which extended like a shelf into the sea. Groves of olive, lemon and orange trees, weighed down by ripened fruit, clung to the lonely hill slopes. A few sheep and goats grazed on a far hill in the cool mountain air. While Uncle Raymond spoke to his mountain caretaker, Sammy investigated the overgrown garden filled with red, pink, and salmon-colored hibiscus fighting a color battle with a myriad of wild flowers.

It seemed that Uncle Raymond kept an eye on the family place when it was unoccupied. Sammy found him in the basement rummaging through stored furniture and singing a favorite Arabic love song. Opening the house for the summer was a bit of a chore but Sammy enjoyed helping Uncle Raymond repair some broken furniture and haul it into the garden. By mid-afternoon the caretaker had opened the shutters and cleaned from top to bottom. Everything looked homey and comfortable. Even though the garden table they had repaired wobbled a bit, Sammy and Uncle Raymond were proud of their work.

After a late lunch of fried chicken and *hommos,* Sammy coaxed his uncle to tell him a story.

"Okay, I'll tell you the popular story of Astarte and Adonis. This is one of the best known Byblos legends which explains the origin of the seasons, particularly the birth of spring."

Uncle Raymond paused as the old caretaker served him his *helou,* or sweet coffee, and then started. "The Roman war god Mars was jealous of the beautiful goddess Astarte's love for a handsome youth named Adonis. He was so consumed with hatred that he sent a wild boar to kill Adonis while the youth was hunting on Mount Lebanon. As he died, grieving Astarte held him in her arms. His blood flowed into the Adonis River, a few kilometers from here. The river was named after him because his blood turned it red."

Uncle Raymond added as an aside, "What is *still* considered a miracle by some is that at the very same time each spring, a particular wind comes up that melts the snows and carries the red earth of these mountains to the sea. Also during spring the mountains are all covered with red flowers — anemones, which legend reminds us are the drops of Adonis' blood."

"Astarte, the earth mother, so mourned her lover's death that the leaves dried and fell from the trees, the weather turned cold, the earth lay barren, and all plants died. For six months Astarte pleaded for the return of her loved one, and finally the gods agreed. But it was a hard bargain, Adonis would come to life and be reunited with Astarte only when the sun crossed the vernal equinox, but only for six months of the year. The other six months he was to live in the underworld."

Sammy's eyes glowed, "Do you mean that each year Adonis returns from the underworld of winter to rejoin Astarte, and that is what brings on spring?"

"Exactly. She is so happy that a great rejoicing occurs throughout the land. It becomes green again, birds sing, flowers bloom, and young animals are born. Love returns to the land. This story is important because it symbolizes the struggle of love and life against death."

"And people celebrated?"

"In the old days thousands of pilgrims traveled to Byblos from all over the Roman Empire. And there were great festivals to celebrate the return of Adonis to earth and the coming of spring. Byblos became the center of his cult, and the seat of the mysteries of the seasonal cycle."

Raymond looked at his watch, "Hey, we better close the house and hurry home. I promised your aunt we'd be home before this." The frantic ride down the mountain in Uncle Raymond's old Mercedes was scary. The hairpin turns and steep ravines made Sammy's head spin, and his stomach!

After dinner he wrote a letter to his parents, and Nina, and drew for them a Roman Bath as he had seen it in one of Uncle Raymond's books. He wrote, "The Romans were famous for their grand baths which were so large they sometimes covered more than an acre of land! They were decorated with marble and bronze statues." Then he drew — after all his practice at the site, he was getting quite good at it — a Roman sponging himself with icy cold water, and another going down marble steps into a large marble pool filled with lukewarm water. The book had explained that such a room was called a *tepidarium,* and Sammy was told by Clovis that that's where we got our word "tepid" for "warm" water. He wrote that the furnaces heating the water were set under the floor in a basement, and that they also provided warm air for the bathers. He drew people entering the hot rooms, the *caldarium.* He had been surprised to read that the Romans then reversed the process by returning to the *frigidarium,* where the pores, cleaned by hot water, were sponged closed with icy-cold water.

He wrote his family all about Sebastian, the games they played amid the temple ruins, the fortress walls, and the gates of the ancient city.

The following noon Sammy found Clovis in Tewfik's café having lunch. Following his plan of studying the site period by period, he asked the archaeologist about the Roman influence in Byblos, and told him he'd been reading up on the history of Rome.

Clovis smiled. "So you're off in the Roman period! I venture to say you won't stop, knowing you, until you know it all!"

"How did Byblos become Roman?"

"In 64 B.C., in the time of the Late Republic, about forty years before the establishment of the Empire under Augustus, the great general Pompey brought Byblos under the strict control of Rome. I think the Byblites heartily welcomed this powerful leadership because gangsters had taken over the city from the weakened control of the last Hellenistic Seleucid period. Pompey set the city free from the gangsters and beheaded them!" This last remark was said with a typical flourish, running his hand across his throat.

Then Clovis carefully described the layout of Romanized Byblos, much of it built under the Empire. It was the same architecture used throughout the Roman world for baths, colonnades, theaters, the Forum and the basilica — all were based on the same principles.

"What is a *basilica?"*

"It was a building where all the public meetings took place. Roman law had long been codified to maintain order, and legal cases were tried in the basilica. It was a very large building. Inside, there was a large room or cella, and at its end was a semicircular apse where the judge sat. Steps and a balustrade separated the apse from the spectators."

Interrupting them, Tewfik came over to the table and challenged Clovis to a game of tric trac. For the past few days, the archaeologist had finally had a winning streak and was confident his luck had changed for good! Sammy knew this was not an appropriate time for more questions, so he whispered to Sebastian, "We'd better sneak out. Clovis always gets so upset if he doesn't win! Come on." Picking up his sketch pad, the boy and his dog left the café and headed for the gate that marked the entrance to the site.

Sebastian led the way down into the ruins. They crossed the small valley in the middle, and strolled up to the rocky promontory that had served for the earlier burials of the Byblos kings. Its edge also had provided a base for a Roman colonnade. Tall thin hollyhocks were in bloom, dressing the promontory in pinky purple. The air up on the rocks was sweet and fresh. From the edge of the colonnade, Sammy looked down on the excavated area. Byblos was his conquest, lying like a map at his feet.

Suddenly Sebastian spied a big tom cat strutting throughout the valley below and took off like a shot. Sammy cried out, "Hey, come back! Stop, Sebastian!" He laughed as he watched Sebastian madly chase the tom across the valley and disappear behind the Temple of Reshef. Sammy rested against a Roman column base and gazed up at the majestic granite columns towering over him. He began to sketch the Roman city Clovis had described to him. Imagine, 8000 miles of Roman roads with arched bridges linking other cities of the Near East to Byblos. At the entrance to the city was the Nymphaeum, a monumental fountain, which met all roads from Syria to the north and east, and south from Israel. The northern port had great wharves, storehouses, and a lighthouse to warn the trading ships that sailed the far reaches of the Empire, which included North Africa and Europe.

Clovis had given him a clear idea of where the Roman theater, the baths, and the law courts had been built over earlier buildings, obliterating any traces of them. Even the temple of the city goddess, Baalat Gebal, now worshipped as Venus, had been modified. But few Roman structures remained because they too had been erased by later builders. Of the Roman period, only this high-placed colonnade and the theater were still standing for him to sketch. He worked for some time.

Then, wondering where his dog had gone, Sammy stood up and scanned the area for Sebastian. Oh, that beast!

Unable to sight the dog, he lay down on the soft grass, stretched out and gazed at the sky. Fuzzy billows of clouds drifted overhead, casting shadows on the site.

A cold nose nudged Sammy's face. Sebastian, full of adventure from his cat chase, had returned to seek Sammy's approval for all the briars he had caught in his long hair. Boy and dog sauntered from the tall colonnade to the theater. Sammy sketched the design of it and made mental notes on what he had read was the difference between a Roman theater and the earlier Greek theaters. Both were magnificent outdoor edifices, but the Greeks always took advantage of a hill to build their theaters into, while the Romans selected the best possible view for their theaters. He remembered that the Greeks performed plays in a circle, in the middle, oddly enough called the *orchestra*, but that the Romans acted from a stage raised about 1.5 meters (five feet) above the *orchestra* and they had backdrops, and scenery.

He loved this theater. He was sitting on one of the marble seats, when Sebastian, who was in the orchestra, let out a bark. It sounded as if the dog were right next to Sammy. What acoustics.

It was time to go home, so together they trudged up the cobblestone streets. They stopped at Tewfik's to see what was going on. Tewfik gave Sammy a glass of juice, and on the tray beside it wrapped in brown paper, was a Roman lamp. "This is for you to take home to your sister."

"Ohhh, Tewfik, I can't accept this. It's not ethical."

"It's a reproduction, a copy, not an antique. It hasn't been excavated or taken out of any archaeological context. It was made yesterday in Saleh's workshop. So don't play indignant archaeologist with me! Besides, its not for you, Sammy, it is a gift from me to your sister. You have no choice in the matter; you must accept it for her. It has the god Adonis molded on the top. It will help your sister know our Byblos too."

Sammy felt embarrassed, but grateful. He was overjoyed with Nina's gift. She would adore the lamp and the face of Adonis. He would have to write to her and tell her all about that god, and also about Adonis and Astarte.

That night at dinner Uncle Raymond presented Sammy with a coin minted in Byblos in 217-218 A.D. under the Emperor Macrinus. Sammy's heart sank. He meant to make no mistakes this time. "Oh, Uncle, it's wonderful!" he exclaimed. "And it has the Roman Temple of Baalat Gebal on its reverse. That's great. Thanks a lot!" Then he added, "But where did you find it?"

Uncle Raymond gave him a bear hug. "I'm glad you like it. And guess what? I beat Clovis at *tric trac* and then, afterwards, I found this coin on the beach! How's that for a lucky day?" Uncle Raymond definitely looked pleased with himself.

Sammy, relieved that the coin had no sealed archaeological context, squeezed his uncle's hand; then he dashed off to make a rubbing of the coin to send to Nina, and put it away in a safe place with the lamp and some of the more special items in his collection.

Clovis, Sammy, Aunt Nadia and Uncle Raymond attend the dance festival at Byblos

CHAPTER 12

The Christian Church

Byzantine Byblos
330-636 A.D.

After his shower, Sammy took special pains in dressing for dinner. An Arab folk dance festival was being held that evening in the ruins. Next to the Crusader castle, a platform had been built and seating for hundreds of people had been erected.

When he was ready, he entered the living room dressed in gray slacks, a white shirt, a striped tie, a light blue blazer and his still new loafers. Everyone whistled.

"I miss your jeans and red shirt," Clovis chuckled.

They were all dressed in their summer finery. Aunt Nadia, Uncle Raymond and Clovis. Clovis, who took any occasion to wear a spiffy suit, was sporting a geranium in his lapel.

During dinner Sammy showed the lamp Tewfik had given Nina so he could ask Clovis for his opinion. "What do you think? Isn't it wonderful?"

"This is a fine lamp. Congratulations, Sammy. Good copies of Roman lamps are hard to come by. Look at the small filling hole for the oil and the small nozzle for the wick."

"How did they make them anyway?" Sammy was turning it over and around quizzically.

"First," said Clovis, "two molds were prepared with the design of the lamp that the potter wanted to create. Soft clay was pressed into each of the two molds, one for the top half and another for the bottom. Just before the clay became stiff and hard, both parts were unmolded, joined together, and the seam closed with wet clay and then smoothed. The lamp was then slipped and..."

"But," Sammy interrupted, "Oh, come on, Clovis, what is this about putting a slip on a lamp? It's just as bad as dressing a stone!"

Everyone but Aunt Nadia was laughing. Clovis began to laugh also, and he translated the joke for Aunt Nadia. She began to giggle with the others and it was contagious, nobody could stop laughing! Sebastian looked around the room and hid under the couch. He thought he had done something wrong.

"At this rate, we'll never make the theater deadline!" complained Clovis waving about his arms. "We better be on our way, Sammy, put Nina's lamp in a safe place." Still laughing, Clovis told Sammy, "'Slip' is a strange expression, I'll admit to that, but it's a term to describe the paint solution that was used to cover the whole vessel."

Sammy peered at his lamp closely, looking for the seam, and found it encircling the widest part.

Clovis went on. "Tomorrow I promise to show you the difference between your lamp and the later shoe-shaped lamps of the Byzantine period."

Nadia interrupted, "My goodness, let's leave or we'll be late."

Everyone hurried out of the house and headed through the shuttered *souk* to reach the entrance of the seating area. About halfway to the improvised theater Sammy asked about Byzantine Byblos, "Clovis, how were they different from the Romans and whatever happened to the Cult of Adonis?"

Clovis said that the Roman cult had been destroyed with the coming of Christianity. "You've heard of the Roman Emperor, Constantine the Great?"

Sammy thought for a moment, then brightening, nodded.

"Briefly, in 330 A.D., Constantine transferred his capital from Rome to Byzantium, the modern Istanbul. He then renamed the city Constantinople, after guess who?"

"Himself, of course," replied Sammy, smiling.

"The change of power," continued Clovis, "from the West to the East marked the beginning of the so-called Byzantine Period. Constantine, as you probably also remember, instead of persecuting the Christians as former Roman emperors had, made Christianity the official religion of the state. During this period, new ideas and new art forms inspired by religious fervor spread across the Empire. People were encouraged to adopt *one* state religion. Officialdom now spent its energy stamping out pagan cults — for example, the cult of Adonis — just as the Romans had previously tried to stamp out Christianity."

Sammy started to say something, but then the music reached his ears and seemed to carry him along. They found their seats. The boy had come to realize that music and dancing were part of the daily lives of the Byblites. The orchestra, composed of elongated tapering drums held under the players'

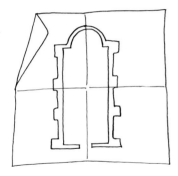

arms, Zithers and reed flutes, began to throb. Two lines of swaying *Debké* dancers in multicolored costumes ran onto the stage and soon held the audience spellbound with their gaiety and energy. The spectators joined in by clapping their hands to the rhythm of the music. A famous singer of Arabic love songs made her appearance and was wildly applauded. Sammy enjoyed watching the people in the audience as much as the singer. They were transfixed by her performance. Clovis translated the words: it was a sad love song. Unlike sad western ballads, this song lasted for more than an hour. But the music all began to sound the same to Sammy and he grew restless. His eyes became heavy and finally closed.

When cheers went up from the crowd, Sammy awoke with a start; one of the people in his dream had looked like the Byblos thief. The singer was taking a bow and her song had finally come to an end. Uncle Raymond was just one of many who stood up and applauded his approval. The setting that night in the moonlight next to the castle couldn't have been more beautiful. Everyone loved the evening.

After Church on Sunday, Sammy asked Clovis about the various religions that had changed the beliefs of the Byblites through different times. And he was curious about his family. "Do any of my relatives have other beliefs?"

"Religion is a very personal thing, Sammy. Today people are free to chose their faith, in Lebanon just as in America." He explained that some of his family were Catholic Maronites, others were Orthodox, and yet another branch of the family had become Moslem.

"Our branch in America are Protestants, Unitarians," Sammy contributed. "Our family alone represents many faiths!"

"That's right," Clovis answered. "If you are interested in the early Church, I suggest that after your Aunt Nadia's lunch, you visit 'Sayidet Naja' a small Byzantine Orthodox chapel. It has been temporarily closed, but you will find a lady caretaker there who will open it for you if you tell her I sent you."

Sammy knew how to get there, but Clovis drew a rough sketch on a paper napkin so he could understand the church's plan.

After lunch, while everyone else took a rest, Sammy, with Sebastian at his side, skipped along the familiar winding route through the funny old cobblestone streets until he arrived at the outside wall of the Byzantine chapel. His pull on the bell cord was answered by a shrivelled old woman who opened the weather-worn wooden gate and allowed him to pass through into a small grassy courtyard.

She highly disapproved of Sebastian but Sammy explained to her that the dog would wait in the courtyard while he himself explored the church.

The woman led him to a vine-covered door which she opened with an enormous key. Since most of the windows were shuttered, she lit a candle which flickered and threw shadows on the bare, white-washed walls and arched roof. It was musty and damp. Standing there, Sammy thought he could smell the ancient incense that had been burnt in the church long ago. He reached into his pocket and pulled out the paper napkin to study it.

"Of course! There *is* something familiar about it all!" he realized.

During the Roman Period, it was in this semi-circular part of the basilica, the apse, where the governor sat to decide legal issues. Or at least that was the way Sammy's mind recognized the plan of the chapel. Clovis had told him that the Christians had chosen the *Basilica* plan — the Roman public meeting house or law court — for their houses of worship because they wanted them to look as different from pagan temples as possible. And more important, because it signified a place where all people could meet freely. And once established in the 4th century A.D., the design was used for nearly 2000 years and is popular even now. Clovis had also told him that in the Byzantine Period, the apse was considered the holiest part of the church, and was reserved for the priests and the sacred objects.

Why, it was the same idea as the Holy of Holies where only the high priest could go in the ancient Temple of Baalat Gebal! He was beginning now to know enough, and understand enough to make connections! Connections between ancient man and modern man. Connections between cultures, civilizations, and ages.

He walked through Clovis' plan, and noted each section very carefully. The three divisions were all there: the *narthex*, the nave, and the apse, just as Clovis had sketched them for him. Under his feet there were traces of the beautiful old mosaic pavement.

Pleased with his understanding, he retraced his steps into the courtyard and fresh air. Sebastian jumped up in greeting. Sammy reached in his pocket to give the old lady a coin, as Clovis had instructed him. Sammy thanked the woman politely.

He walked over to the excavation house. There was always work to be done. "Work, work, and more work," was what Clovis always said. Sammy watched chain-smoking Abu Hanna carefully restoring a pot, fixing piece upon piece to rebuild the old, broken pot. What patience he had. Such a private person, tiny Abu Hanna. It seemed that he didn't want anyone to know anything about him. Clovis was poring over plans. He was a small man as well, but muscular and strong. Sammy didn't want to be a nuisance, so he quietly sat down to wait. When the archaeologist finally finished his "Sunday work," as he called it, they started talking about Byzantine Byblos — art, churches, even pirates and merchants.

While putting away his work sheets, Clovis explained, "You remember that Raymond told you the story of Wenamon. With the end of Egyptian power in about 1100 B.C., when the Egyptians were unable to pay for cedar any more, Byblos lost its commercial cedar trade — that was the principal source for the city's growth and importance, you remember, in 3000 B.C. In the Byzantine period, trade continued to bring some wealth to Byblos, but larger cities like Beirut became so popular that Byblos found itself an exchange center of only minor importance."

Changing the subject, he remembered, "Didn't I promise to show you Byzantine lamps? Let's ask Abu Hanna to show you some from the excavation."

Abu Hanna was kind and helpful. Taking his keys, he led them into the back of the storeroom where he unlocked a cabinet that was filled with pottery lamps.

He remarked, "You'll recognize these Christian motifs, palm branches, a cross, and a candlestick!"

Abu Hanna handed a lamp to Clovis, who turned it in his hand and said, "Oh, yes, here's one which bears an ancient Greek inscription around the raised center and filling hole for the oil."

"What does it say? Can you read it?" Sammy asked.

Clovis glowed with pride. "Of course! A good Near Eastern archaeologist has to know Greek!" The restorer and the boy peered down at the lamp as Clovis pieced together the words. "Translated, it reads, 'THE LIGHT OF CHRIST SHINES FOREVER WEll'."

Looks of delight spread over the faces of his audience. They were both very impressed with his easy ability to read ancient Greek.

"Just one of the tools of an archaeologist," he muttered, with a show of modesty.

Then Abu Hanna, in his gentle voice, asked Clovis if Sammy had ever seen a Byzantine cross. All the crosses from the excavation had been moved to the National Museum, but he knew Assad, the blind shopkeeper, had one.

"Yellah. Let's go before the souk tourist shops close," said Clovis.

They affectionately bid Abu Hanna farewell. Sammy wondered if Clovis had forgotten that most of his nasty remarks about looters and vandals were directed to the shopkeepers in the old town, since it was they who illegally sold antiquities.

When they reached the artisans' alley, Clovis led the way into one of the old souk shops where he noisily hailed blind Assad who was waiting on a French-speaking customer. Clovis immediately made himself at home by going behind the counter and showing Sammy highly, ornamented brass daggers and brightly-embroidered table cloths.

There was hardly room to turn around, and the tourist was determined to see every scarf in the place. But after the scarf sale was made, Clovis quietly asked his friend Assad, "Can we go upstairs? I want to show my friend your early Byzantine cross."

Assad beckoned them to follow and led them to the back of the dilapidated shop. They all scrambled up rickety stairs, and arrived at his lodgings.

"Look there!" proudly pointed the sightless merchant.

On the white-washed wall of a very grand bedroom, hung a beautiful bronze cross. Moving toward it, he said, "You can see that this 7th century cross is shaped somewhat differently from today's crosses. These four wide arms narrow as they meet in the center." His hands lovingly followed its lines. Assad took it down and placed it in Sammy's hands. Holding it with great care, Sammy studied its shape. There was a circle on the end of each arm and another in its very center. "Oh, how ancient this is," he barely breathed, then handed it back ceremoniously to Assad.

Assad said, "This cross has been in our family for years. Sadly, we have no idea where it came from. Perhaps Byblos — we just don't know." To Clovis he continued, "We used to be collectors and dealers, but we are not any more. Ask Clovis."

Sammy quickly murmured, "Of course, I know."

"Perhaps you would enjoy looking at my wall hangings. Let me offer you a drink. This tapestry..."

The ring of a bell sounded from downstairs. "Oh! Business calls! I must tend to the late tourists, but please stay here as long as you like."

Sammy held his breath as blind Assad scurried down the steps.

After re-examining the cross and giving the tapestries a glimpse, Sammy and Clovis went downstairs. Sure enough, a tourist invasion had taken place and all were bargaining for momentos of Byblos. He was amazed at the way Assad lived and worked. Sammy waited until there was a proper moment, "Thank you, *Chukran*, Mr. Assad, for showing me such beautiful things."

Assad extended a friendly hand to the boy.

"It was great to see the cross. It was mind-blowing! In Boston that means it was a fantastic experience!"

Assad was sorry that Sammy could not stay for a cold drink — another time perhaps.

Outside, Sebastian was waiting. Boy and dog left Clovis and sauntered up the narrow street, stopping to gaze into quaint shop windows. Smiling dealers, closing up their shops, greeted the now familiar pair.

The next moment Sammy saw a burly stranger coming rapidly towards him. As they passed, the stranger snarled, "If you meet one of us again, you will never get home alive!"

Sammy stepped out from the sidewalk into the street, looking quickly and keenly all around him. The stranger must have ducked into one of the shops, for there was no sign of him. The street was filled with tourists and late afternoon shoppers, but he didn't know where the stranger would be hiding. He ran for his life. When he arrived home, he rushed to his room and out on to the balcony and sat for a spell, his mind filled with the snarling stranger's threat. Sebastian followed, threw himself down and fell asleep. Sammy knew he had to tell Clovis about it. His thoughts then turned to Byzantine Byblos and Assad's hospitality, but more particularly, to the blind man's friendly hand.

"Isn't it all unbelievable, Sebastian?" Sammy patted the dog. On hearing his name and feeling his master's touch, the dog raised his head, wagged his tail, but then promptly returned to his nap.

Sammy and 'the gang' on the beach at Byblos

CHAPTER 13

In a Cave

The First Arab Period
636-1108 A.D.

A heated political discussion was going on among Clovis, Uncle Raymond, and Tewfik in the coffee house. Sammy enjoyed hearing their views because each was so passionately interested in history, philosophy and religion. When today's affairs bored them, they would lapse into discussions of many yesterdays ago. When Sammy came in, Clovis, with bulldog determination, was waving his arms around, excitedly making a point. This time it was about the Islam religion or, as it is often called, Mohammedanism. Seeing Sammy, he proclaimed, "Mohammedanism, the concept of Islam, was founded in Arabia by Mohammed in 622 A.D. It really started with the *hejira*."

"Hij... what?" Sammy asked.

Clovis replied, "Okay, I'll explain. Mohammed was preaching and seeking converts in his home town, Mecca, but the people disliked him for his religious claims and his attacks on their way of life. So in 622 they drove him out of the city and he fled to Medina where he was welcomed. This journey is known as the *hejira* and is considered so important to Moslems that they date their calendar from it."

Sammy joined in, "But why did this religion attract so many believers, and so quickly?"

"Because the Prophet stated three ideas simply and clearly: first, there is but one God, and his name is Allah; second, there is but one commander of the faithful and he is Mohammed, who rules the earth; third, the word of God, which was delivered to Mohammed by Allah, is the *Koran*, or Moslem Holy Book. He preached that belief in these three simple principles would bring enlightenment and salvation. That was potent stuff for people who had known only primitive forms of religion before, such as animism."

"What in the world is animism?" asked Sammy.

"It's believing that a spirit lives in an inanimate object, such as a tree or a stone, and worshiping it."

"What does the Moslem Holy Book say?"

"Many things. That most important of all are the five principal duties every good Moslem undertakes: First, they must know and recite the religion's creed; second, they must worship five times a day, directing their prayers to Mecca, the Moslem holy city; third, they must fast — not eat — from sunrise to sunset during the month of Ramadan, the holy month, that is determined by the lunar calender; fourth, they must give alms and help the poor; and fifth, they must make a pilgrimage or what they call a *hadj* to Mecca in Saudi Arabia once in their lifetime."

No one could stop Clovis now; he was like an overloaded switchboard. "Yes, the Moslem believes God has shown himself to mankind through prophets, and three of these prophets have been given a book from God. To Moses, God gave the Law. To Jesus, He gave the Gospel. And to Mohammed, the last of the prophets, He gave the Koran. That's why people who follow these three religions — Judaism, Christianity, and Islam, are known as people of The Book."

Shaggy Sebastian was bored. He curled up under one of the tables and napped.

Sammy leaned forward eagerly: "How did Islam spread? Like Christianity?"

Uncle Raymond chimed in, "Yes, and it was also spread by the sword, by conquest. That is, the rise of Moslem power was brought about by a series of highly successful military invasions. From 634 to 712 A.D., they conquered an empire which stretched from the borders of China and India in the east almost into the heart of Western Europe! They swept across North Africa, up through Spain, and were finally stopped only 127 miles south of Paris!"

"Wow! Paris! That far?" Sammy became thoughtful. "All that conquering, all those converts, in about a hundred years! There are too many dates for me; can I write these conquests down?"

"Great idea, we'll put them down right now!" Clovis was in his element. Tewfik went over to the juice stand and returned with paper and pen, put them in front of Clovis, and sat down to mull over dates, which were not his specialty.

The archaeologist took great pride in his Arabic writing. To him, it was an art form. Sammy knew that the script was a very difficult thing to master. He watched Clovis carefully position his arm and begin to make notes. First he wrote from right to left, in Arabic, the title, 'The Military Conquests of Islam.' Underneath he wrote the same, in English, from left to right.

Uncle Raymond led off. "Let's start with Damascus, the capital of Syria which fell in 635 A.D."

Tewfik gave his well-thought-out contribution, "Jerusalem was taken in either 637 or 638, and when Jerusalem surrendered, the whole of Palestine fell."

There was silence as Clovis made a notation of the dates of military exploits. Uncle Raymond, looked at the paper and was able, at least, to read the Arabic numerals and said, "If I remember correctly, that was the same year they conquered the whole Persian Empire!"

Clovis looked up from his work, "No, I'm sure that it fell earlier than that!"

Tewfik defended Uncle Raymond, which made Clovis furious. "I'm going to find out!" he said and began to stomp out of the café.

Tewfik caught him by the arm and said easily, "What difference does it make? Let's go to my house where we can look it up in my encyclopedia amid all the comforts of home."

He lived just a stone's throw away. Patting Sammy on the back, he winked at Uncle Raymond, and said, "Come, Sammy, let me show you a real Arabic house."

As the party of four walked through the winding street, the friends continued their little argument, and by the time they arrived at the old mosque, the men lost Sammy in a new discussion of Islamic art. He gathered that Eastern ideas of art were blended with Western, to result in a beautiful flowing Arabic style that was basically ornamental. Patterns were curved and angular, floral and abstract. The human form only was not portrayed. He thought he knew that much, that in Islam it wasn't allowed. They then spoke of the castle that was built by Banu Ammar, the Emir of Tripoli.

Tewfik added, "The size of the keep and the guard towers were impressive."

By then the group had arrived at Tewfik's two-story old house which was surrounded by a high wall that hid a secret garden filled with fig trees and flowering plants. Sammy sighed in admiration. On entering the living room he was astonished to find so little furniture: two small low tables, an inlaid box in the corner and along three walls, built-in bench-like sofas with cushions with oriental rugs tossed over them. He was fascinated by a low marble fountain which actually bubbled away in the center of the room.

Tewfik led them through this centrally placed living room and into his study which displayed a collection of colored Arabic glass decorated with inscriptions. An ornate glass *nargilé*, or water pipe, stood in the corner of this cozy study. Beautiful young Margo, Tewfik's niece, served them sweets and thick Arabic coffee, and Sammy had a soda.

After a bit of chatter, the men began leafing through the encyclopedia. "Raymond's date is right!" trumpeted Tewfik. One of his great pleasures in life was proving Clovis wrong in anything. Beating him at *tric trac* wasn't enough!

Naturally, this did not appease Clovis until he had seen the date for himself. "I give in!" He broke into a smile. Then, pulling the note paper out, he grumbled, "Let's get on with it."

Uncle Raymond began reading, "'The entire province of Syria (of which Byblos was a part), was conquered in 636 A.D.'"

"Did Byblos change much when it was conquered by Islam?"

Clovis answered the boy. "Yes, Sammy. The people adopted Arab dress, customs, rules, even language — just as if it were part of their own tradition. But in spite of all these new ideas, Byblos became a dull and provincial place. It lost all its remaining reputation as a center of culture."

"But," interrupted Uncle Raymond, "They stubbornly refused to change their religion. They remained Christian in the old Byzantine tradition!"

"I think," mused Sammy, "that it was wise of the Moslem rulers to leave them free to make that choice for themselves." He thought of how in-

tolerant the Christians had been of the ancient pagan religions.

Wrapped up in their discussion, the men didn't notice a little later when Sammy quietly left the room. In the excitement of all the talk, he'd completely forgotten about Sebastian. Had he left the dog in the café? As he ran down the steps and through the garden, he saw a familiar black tail sticking through the grill of the outside gate. "Sorry, old boy." Sammy led the dog into the house.

Looking at the men, he asked, "Did you finish with all the dates?"

"Yes, and here you are, great scholar to be: dates in English and in Arabic!" Clovis grandly read the list to Sammy. "Let's see, in 642 A.D. the city of Alexandria and all of Egypt became Arab, and by 650 the armies of Islam had sailed into the Mediterranean and captured the island of Cyprus which had been an important control point for the Byzantines. Later, there was the conquest of the islands of Crete and Sicily. The only stumbling block was the Byzantine capital, Constantinople..."

Sammy gratefully took the paper, "Thanks very much. I'll memorize this by dinner," he said kiddingly.

He carefully folded the paper and put it in his pocket. As Tewfik had to get back to business, Sammy decided that he and Sebastian had adventure awaiting them and they took off to find 'the gang' and explore the limestone caves along the water's edge.

"Now, let's see, Sebastian, first let's rustle up Wasfi. Wouldn't it be great to find some pirate treasure?" Sebastian hardly heard his master. He had dashed off down the street to lead the way.

Sammy took serious Wasfi away from a history book. Down the street and around the corner, they found athletic 'Krazy Jamil' wearing his 'shades' and a black T-shirt with a motorcycle pictured on the front. He was knocking a soccer ball about with forgiving Hamid. For his part, Hamid was happy to be taken off the hook, for Jamil was running circles around him.

The four dodged like Indian scouts along the coast. Whenever they got together it was a few hours of carefree madness. There was the usual rough-housing, shouting, laughter, hiding among the rocks, getting each other wet, fighting, arguing, jumping, throwing stones and of course, swearing. They enthusiastically taught Sammy words they all knew, and corrected his pronunciation until he got it right. Out of parents' earshot, they yelled words in unison and used them to punctuate every thought.

One by one they struggled around, up, and down the steep rocks; shoving each other around, they were anxious to explore scary caves, but each had to control his anxiety because, in truth, they were terrified of their adventures. The thrill of it all was part of their self-imposed 'gang' discipline.

'The gang' reached a rocky barren area that stretched a kilometer (more than half a mile) north of Byblos. Few people, except for them, ever came here, but there was a myriad of hiding places and caves. They went to the rock they had christened "The Margo," after Tewfik's pretty niece. They had marked it with an X as a secret, permanent record of their friendship.

They reached familiar caves and walked in and out of them, hooting and howling as they liked to do. Quiet Wasfi decided to hide and wandered deep into a cave, feeling the sides as he went. To his amazement, he found a coin, and then he moved his hand around on the ledge and found more! They looked like gold — the goldness shone in the dim light. He yelled to 'the gang', "Hey, come! I've found some gold coins!"

"I can't believe it." said the astonished Hamid as they examined the treasure together. He counted them carefully, "Seventeen! Fantastic!"

Wasfi said, "They're dinars inscribed in Arabic."

"Let's study them later, Wasfi. I'm bored. Let's explore for more," said Jamil.

But Wasfi was too excited. He thought they had found a ship's treasure which had been pirated sometime in the 8th century, the century of the Arabs' great expansion. He read the Arabic inscription, "God the almighty is one. He was not conceived and not born." Looking up he said, "Ahhh, this was taken from the Koran."

After warnings from Sammy about the antiquities laws, and great arguments, all agreed they would take the treasure to Clovis. Sammy wrapped the collection in the paper that listed the dates, and gave it to Wasfi for safekeeping, because he had the best pockets.

'The gang' then decided to have naval operations. There was the sound of a trawler's engine. Excitedly they took it as a navy coastal search vessel and quickly hid in a cave entrance, waiting until the boat had passed them and went out of sight. Of course, the trawler was the enemy, and they conspired to attack its home base. They formed a search party to find the enemy cave. Going well beyond the usual caves, they found it and went inside. Sure enough, there was food, bedding, dynamite, and Hamid found a gun.

"Wait a minute, I'll show you something! Hey, look here!" Jamil called.

A shock of revelation came to Sammy. Barely visible, there they were, stacks of artifacts centuries old. His eyes strained in the darkness. It was unbelievable. He knew what they had to do.

It seemed very quiet.Only the wash of the sea could be heard. He whispered instructions. Not wanting to be seen by the trawler captain, they decided not to go the way they had come, but to manoeuver through the fields back to town. Un-naturally silent, 'the gang' closed ranks and quickly made a foray up the cliff.

They found Uncle Raymond who heard their stories — first about the cave and then about Wasfi's coins. He escorted them to the police station where the black-haired police chief made notes of the cave incident. Anyway, they had done what they thought they should do. Now the rest was up to the police.

The Crusaders arrive by sea and by land at Byblos

CHAPTER 14   Embriaci vs. Bohemond

Crusader Gibelet
1108-1299 A.D.

A few days later, Sammy was playing Crusaders vs. Arabs, a game like Cowboys and Indians, on top of the high Crusader castle walls. He and Sebastian were spending a thoroughly enjoyable afternoon hiding from 'the gang,' in and out of various parts of the castle where Sammy continued to imagine he was a Knight of the Cross. Sighting the enemy through the loop holes, slits in the walls of the towers, the boy pretended he was an archer, his long bow sturdily defending the city. Sebastian joined in by poking his nose through slits to sniff out the foe.

Sometimes Sammy felt happiest in the secret rooms of the castle's ground floor, built with beautiful barrel-vaulted ceilings. More exciting, however, were the narrow steep staircases and the

Crusader drawbridge, now a ramp, leading from the Crusader town into the fortress. These really excited his imagination. He was comforted by the huge underground cistern, which would provide water if there was to be a long siege. He could almost hear the enemy approaching, striving to cross the moat, encircling the castle walls. It would take all his energy, his cunning, to plan the defense, to protect the two entrances of the castle.

With Sebastian tagging behind, he descended down into the deep dry moat. As he marched around the walls, inspecting them for any weak spots, he warned Sebastian of the dangers. "We're not sure of our situation here, so follow me, and don't make a sound!"

Then he dashed up the small winding stairway.

Arriving at a central keep chamber, he examined his position. "Here we'll definitely be secure," he announced. The keep was the most interesting part of the castle to Sammy. It was solidly constructed with huge Roman stones. It was the strongest part of the castle; if all else failed, he and Sebastian could make a last stand here. "Psst! Sebastian! I think we beat them! Let's inspect the damage."

Together, they loped down the stairs, surveyed all the fallen bodies in the courtyard — Christian and Saracen — and made their way to the outer castle area. The 'inspection' amused Clovis who had been observing these military maneuvers. Spotting the archaeologist, the boy signalled to the dog that the battle was won. In triumph, he hailed the approaching compatriot.

The two strolled to the promontory and climbed to its highest point. "Clovis, look at the castle in the setting sun. It is so grand."

"Yes, it was the only one in Lebanon to remain in possession of its original feudal family from the beginning of the Crusades to the end. How would you like to talk about the Crusades, Sammy?"

"Sure I already know that Byblos is the only walled town remaining in Lebanon today that goes back to Crusader times."

Gazing out to sea, Clovis said, "Right! Now let's pretend we're standing here in the spring of 1103. We would witness an amazing sight, both on land and on sea. Out there, on the water, we would be astonished to see a fleet of forty warships stretching all the way down the coast."

Sammy's eyes glowed. "Forty warships! But whose side were they on?"

"AHA, that's just the point! Wait and see." He continued: "Now, naturally, if we were the first to spot the flotilla, we would have hurried to signal the authorities. The news would have flashed its way all through the winding streets and little lanes of the town. Some of the people would have raced to the Land Gate to escape. But, once there, they would have seen colorful banners fluttering in front of columns of armored soldiers advancing on the city."

Sammy was awed. "At the same time!"

Clovis nodded. "Attacks by land and by sea. Can you imagine what the peaceful citizens must have felt? The people of Byblos naturally knew about the Crusades, but had reasoned that since they were already Christian, they certainly wouldn't be conquered in the name of Christianity. Just imagine their confusion! Running about, gathering in frantic groups — weeping women — panicked citizens all asking, 'What are we to do?'" Clovis' eyes grew wide with the excitement of his own story. His fingers played with his worry beads.

"After a great deal of discussion, a group of citizens was selected to meet with the commanders of the would-be conquering force. Do you know, Sammy, we actually have a factual report that this little group of peaceful citizens determined two conditions upon which they would open the city gates: one — the Christian invaders had to provide safe passage for any who wished to leave the city, and two — for those who chose to remain, the right to live peacefully. And, after deliberating, the Crusader admiral accepted the terms and the people of Byblos peaceably surrendered."

Sammy was almost as excited as Clovis, and said, "Who were the Crusaders? Any of them Richard the Lion-Hearted?"

"No, These weren't the English, French or Germans. These men were sailing from north Italy, from the great merchant city of Genoa. They were Genoese, under the command of a most famous knight of valor, named Hugh di Embriaco. He was the Admiral, the High Commissioner for the waters of the so-called 'Republic in Levantine.' Before coming to Byblos, Hugh di Embriaco had commanded seventy Genoese ships in an attack on Tripoli against the Arab Banu Ammar in 1103. When this failed, he sailed down the coast with forty vessels and took Byblos instead."

"How long did the... What did you call them?... the 'Embris' rule?"

"The Embriaci family ruled Gibelet, the Crusader name for Byblos, wisely and well for 200 years, and even after Tripoli fell in 1289, Gibelet continued under the Embriaci rule for another ten years. There was but one interruption; a ten-year interval beginning in 1187 when Gibelet was occupied by that great Arab commander, Saladin.

"How did he come to get Byblos?" asked Sammy.

"Lord Hugh di Embriaco III had been taken his prisoner and, as ransom, the Embriaci had to give up Byblos. The Christian Byblites kept creating problems for Saladin; they were so difficult to manage and rule that in 1190 he was fed up and completely destroyed the town walls and castle. Finally Saladin sold it back to the Embriaci family for 6000 Byzantine gold bezants."

"In school we studied Saladin," said Sammy.

"Come to think of it," Clovis said, "Saladin died a poor man because he spent all his money starting universities in the Near East. At a time when most of the Crusaders couldn't read or write, even the nobility!"

Sammy asked, "What happened then? How did they educate here?"

"The clergy, of course. In the Western world, the Church was the custodian of learning. As a matter of fact, part of that tradition remains in Byblos today, for the Maronites have a monastery located next to the Crusader church."

"Who are the Maronites?"

"They are one of the largest and most ancient of all Christian sects in Lebanon. Even today, most all of Byblos is Maronite. Originally they were a Syriac religious group that had some relations with Rome during Crusader days, but for many years now, they have had communion with the Pope in Rome. Traditionally, the President of Lebanon is a Maronite."

"O Clovis, let's get back to the Crusades. I know the Crusaders had a lot of clout in Europe when they returned, but what kind of changes did they make in Byblos? Good or bad?"

"Judge for yourself! Under the eight-pointed Embriaci star, Byblos changed from the dull provincial little town it had become under the Arab conquest 500 years before, to once again being an international mart. But this time, instead of cedar and papyrus, they traded in spices, wines and locally-made textiles — fine linens.

"Sounds like it once again became a prosperous city."

"Yes. Even though the cedar forests had all but been exhausted of their supply. But Byblos thrived, and was filled with flower gardens. There were great wharves and warehouses built down at the water side, taverns, and the *souk* shopping area. The city was built up again, all thanks to that medieval genius of Genoese commerce, stimulating the ancient Phoenician trading spirit."

"What did the town look like then?"

"Well, the Genoese erected a new walled city, built over a much larger area. The area of the ancient site from the Neolithic to the Hellenistic and Persian periods, and the old town of later Roman, Byzantine and Arab periods, were absorbed. They became part of the Crusader city. Even the port and north harbor and a new city wall, the one we use today, were reconstructed by the Crusaders. Those two towers down there marked the harbor entrance, and those sea walls along there they built to connect the port area to the new city walls." Clovis pointed to the half-ruined towers which stood silent watch over the now small-again port where a string of fishing boats was pushing out of the harbor for the evening catch.

As they settled down on the low parapet wall, Clovis said, "Okay, shoot, Sammy. I know you are bursting with questions, and I always like to be the answer man." (His favorite role!) Sebastian yawned, stretched, curled into his favorite black ball position, and snoozed right off.

"Tell me something about the Crusaders. I get the different Crusades, the leaders and whatever they accomplished, all mixed up. Just who were they and what good did they ultimately do?"

Laughing, Clovis said, "You really do think of questions. Okay, I'll tell you what I can — what I know about them, and their spirit. Now — who were they? Of course they were men, mostly knights and adventurers, of the European or western part of the Empire known as the Holy Roman Empire. They came from France, Germany, Austria, Italy, and England. They were encouraged by the Pope to join together and fight the 'infidel,' fight to recover for Christianity the Moslem-controlled Holy

Land and give protection to those making the pilgrimage to the Holy Shrine."

"Of course, the idea spread like wildfire throughout Europe. The idea 'Crusade' appealed to princes and paupers, priests and scalawags, farmers and burghers — in short, to a complete cross-section of European society. They sewed cloth crosses on their tunics, and took off. Some truly religious people left their homes to fight for the land Christ knew, a land they cherished and dreamed of making a pilgrimage to. And there were knights known as 'Iron men' by the suits of armor they wore. Many of them were renowned for their strength and courage."

"Aha! Richard the Lion-hearted would be considered an 'Iron Man!'"

"Yes, Sammy, you've got it. Also, travel and the lure of the mysterious East, with its riches and spices and, what they didn't know yet, a much higher, indeed more comfortable, level of civilization, appealed to others. But there were greedy, materialistic men who wanted to conquer land and riches for their own personal gain. Naturally, this group had no intention of serving anyone but themselves! They took the Cross merely for their own ends. Yes, there were self-seekers even in those times of greatest religious fervor and sacrifice."

As the Mediterranean dusk was fading, Clovis suggested they get down the steep stairs quickly before it became too dark to see. Walking toward the center of town, he said, "Historians divide the campaigns into six Crusades."

Arriving at the beautiful Crusader church dedicated to St. John the Baptist, 'Mar Yuhanna,' Sammy asked, "When was this built?"

"In 1215," replied Clovis, pointing to the porch-like baptistry and said, "Now, this part, the baptistry, may have been built later. Look closely at its round dome and the delicate lines of the carved zigzags and rosettes in these arches."

Once inside, Clovis waved his arm at the graceful cross-ribbed vaulted roof which Sammy figured out for himself must have been Gothic architecture, by look of the vaulting. "Those great columned piers separate the nave from the two side aisles. Note that the stones are decorated by hammered diagonal lines."

"I know, that's how they were dressed," Sammy snickered.

Clovis paid no attention to this comment, and continued, "See, here's a mason's mark. Masons carved their own individual marks upon the surfaces so they would get paid for cutting the stone..." A motion caught his eye — "Ohh, look who's over there," he said.

"Hey, Sebastian, get out!" Sammy ordered.

The dog was strutting up the aisle to the north

nave and its Romanesque apse, but at the sound of Sammy's voice, turned and loped out the door.

On the following day, Sammy, with one of Wasfi's history books, wandered back to the castle, as though drawn there. He started to read about Byblos and soon was transported back to Crusader Byblos. A fierce rivalry existed between Byblos, the vassal city, and Tripoli; that is, between the Embriaci of Gibelet and another prominent Crusader family, the Bohemonds of Tripoli.

Sammy read that the Embriaci family went against the deceitful French Bohemonds controlling Tripoli. How those two families hated each other. An angry hot-blooded Embriaco decided to defend the family honor and planned a personal attack upon the Bohemonds at Tripoli. But clever Bohemond discovered the plan and bribed a group of peasants near Byblos to ambush Embriaco and chop off his head. This gory deed done, a blood feud broke out consuming the two families.

Later, yet another Bohemond quarreled with an Embriaco, who burned down one of the Bohemonds' castles. This was too much for the Bohemonds; they decided to lead their army against the Embriaci. It was a bloody battle that ended in a draw — and a truce. But Embriaco was not satisfied with the truce, and bloody battles continued. Bohemond, being a wretch and a scoundrel, marched Guy Embriaco and his brothers outside Tripoli, threw them into a ditch — and buried them up to their necks. They were cruelly left there to starve to death while the others who had fought with Guy had their eyes gouged out.

"What did this have to do with Christianity!" Sammy asked himself.

Then he read aloud to Sebastian, that, shortly afterwards, brutal Bohemond visited Byblos to show his muscle and to stop any possible riots against him; and finally, weakened by such petty warrings, Tripoli was leveled to the ground in 1289 by a group known as 'Mameluke Muslims.' "Serves the Bohemonds right." Sammy patted the dog and Sebastian seemed to heartily agree.

The book went on to say that finally, in 1299, the Embriaci also bowed to the complete control of the Mameluke Sultan and abandoning Gibelet, they sailed off to Cyprus. They waited there for some time, then realized there was no hope of regaining the city, so they sailed back to Genoa. Putting his book down, Sammy wondered what the Crusades had accomplished anyway, since by the sixth one the Crusaders had lost everything they'd gained in the *first* one. Later that day at the coffee house Clovis answered his question.

"What good did they do? Well, most important of all, they opened up communications and trade between the world of the East and the world of the West by returning with many products of the more highly-developed East."

"Such as what?"

"Such as damask silk, paper, cotton from India and Egypt, porcelains from China that Europe wasn't able to duplicate until the 18th century, colored glass, mirrors — and foods like rhubarbs, artichokes, rice, sugar, lemons. And, most prized of all, spices, to help alleviate the taste of rotten meat they had to eat in the days before refrigeration. This led to the setting-up of the great spice routes, which made such merchant cities as Venice fabulously wealthy, which eventually led to the discovery of America, because Columbus was trying to find a cheaper, easier sea route to the East than the long arduous overland caravan routes!"

"Yeah, I knew about Columbus. You mean Europe had never had those things before, not even sugar?" Sammy couldn't believe it.

Clovis shook his head. "No, just honey. And do you realize how many Arabic words were introduced? To name but a few: admiral, alcohol, algebra, muslin, sofa, tariff, zenith." He clipped them off in a neat alphabetical order.

"What else?"

"Oh yes, new concepts! Such as the windmill. Can you imagine Holland without its windmills? And Arabic sciences, especially mathematics: Arabic numbers — the Arabs adopted these from Indian mathematics. And navigation, with the Arab invention of the astrolabe, and maps, and celestial navigation too. And a greatly advanced concept of medicine. And new architectural techniques, and so much more. There was a re-evaluation of history; western Europe finally learned about the cradle of its own civilization! It was thanks to the Arabs that the West finally saw again the great classics of Greece: learned about Plato and especially Aristotle, whose teaching was to influence Medieval thought from then on. Not since the fall of the Roman Empire did the West have access to the Greek Classics and philosophy, or even realized they existed!"

"Okay, I'll bite. So how did the Arabs know about the Greeks?"

"Because when they conquered Egypt, in Alexandria, for example, they found great centers of learning, libraries and universities already established. International banking systems were set up by the Arabs, because of the tremendous development of trade, and there was a greater use of gold currency."

"I never knew Europe was so far behind the times." Sammy sounded almost downcast. "How many Crusaders got back safely?"

"Unfortunately, during the 300-year struggle, over two million died from war, famine, disease, and from fighting each other!"

"That's as great a loss as a modern-day world war!" said Sammy. Worried about this, Sammy and Sebastian made their way home.

Mameluke officials swagger along the main street in medieval Byblos

CHAPTER 15

Discovery in the Cave

Mameluke Byblos
1299-1516 A.D.

"Why does Mameluke literally mean 'owned'?" asked Sammy who was sitting next to Clovis in the newly-excavated area.

Sebastian trotted up to Clovis' chair and dropped a stick at his feet, backed up a few steps, and barked expectantly. Clovis threw the stick and said, "Because the Mamelukes were originally slave soldiers, mostly Turks from Russia, the Caucasus, and Central Asia, who were hired and owned by the Ayyubid Sultans who governed Egypt. The fiercely independent Mamelukes, however, became a large part of the army and so strong that they took control away from the Ayyubid Arabs, and forced the overthrow of countries like Egypt. Then they, in turn, proceeded to drive the Crusaders from the Holy Lands. For the next 200 years they ruled Egypt and the surrounding territory."

Sammy started off on a long leisurely ramble along the sea. After he had been walking for some time, he realized he was quite alone and decided he'd better retrace his steps to find Sebastian. After a few minutes of back-tracking, he heard the dog's "I've cornered a cat" bark and ran to the sound. Sure enough, shaggy Sebastian had chased a big black tom cat to the base of a cliff. The cornered cat spat and the dog barked hysterically; it seemed as if neither knew what to do next. Sammy let out a sharp call, which distracted Sebastian long enough for the cat to scramble up the bluff of hard-packed earth. And, of course, the dog had to chase the cat, with Sammy struggling behind, trying to keep up.

Sebastian was making a terrible racket. The boy

took a guess that the clever cat had outsmarted him. Sure enough, the cat had escaped through a small opening high up in the cliff face. But the dog couldn't give up now — so, precariously perched, he dug away at the opening, when suddenly something happened. A huge section of the cliff began to fall away.

Realizing he was in the direct line of the falling earth, Sammy threw himself to the side to keep from being swept down the cliff. There was a roaring crescendo as a mass of earth and rubble picked him up and carried him like a rag doll down to the beach below. And Sammy didn't see the stone which came tumbling down and knocked him unconscious. His body went limp and rolled to one side. After a long black moment, he fought back to consciousness, opened his eyes and felt waves of dizziness and shock course over him. He closed his eyes again. Waited. Then popped them open and slowly pulled to a sitting position. Groaning, he was enormously relieved to find he was all right except for a painful swelling on the back of his head and the beginnings of an awful headache.

Still shaky, Sammy got up slowly, brushed the dirt off, and glanced at the large mound of fallen debris on the beach. Then he peered up to see where it had come from and was astounded to find that the landslide had revealed what looked to be a large cavern. He shouted, "Sebastian! Where are you?" Fearing the worst, he crawled up the sharp

incline and called the dog again. The answering yelp from deep within the cave was a wonderful sound!

Breathing heavily, he reached the entrance. "Sebastian!" he shouted. "Oh, you've been hurt! Hold on, boy, I'll get you free from this mess." A stunned Sebastian was lying under a pile of broken pottery. Sammy couldn't believe his eyes, hundreds of jars lay all about. Ancient-looking jars of every variety lying everywhere, very deep into the cave and above on ledges. While uncovering Sebastian, he realized that his dog had seriously hurt his paw and would need help.

Leaving poor Sebastian behind, Sammy picked his way down the bluff and sped to the excavation house. Clovis wasn't there and neither was Abu Hanna. And not in the coffee house. In vain he searched. Then he ran home to Uncle Raymond to, at least, tell him the news. Uncle Raymond could hardly believe his ears, so together they went off to find Artine, the site supervisor. The three of them hurried back to the beach and struggled up the embankment.

The men were spellbound. Artine was the first to find his voice, "I... I can hardly believe it! Why, this is a national treasure!" Thinking aloud, he said, "I must report this to Monsieur Dunand immediately. He'll have to get a top draftsman and chief restorer, Abu Hanna, here at once!" Cautiously he examined some of the pottery. "This is incredible! There appear to be vessels from so many different periods — well over 200 pieces are here!" Artine straightened up and declared solemnly, "I must return to the dig house. I hope I can catch Monsieur Dunand before he leaves for Beirut. But, anyway, I'll notify the specialists so work can begin at once!"

Turning to Sammy, the elderly Lebanese declared, "Good work, young archaeologist!" Artine then asked them to please watch the cave until he returned, and by all means keep it a secret until he had a chance to officially report it. "This is a spectacular find," he said as he patted the boy on the back.

Uncle Raymond winked at Sammy and beamed, "Congratulations!" And then he added, "But you really look terrible! What happened? How did you find all of this anyway?" waving his arm to take in the treasure.

When Artine had gone, Sammy related his adventure to Raymond. "If it hadn't been for Sebastian, and, yes, that black cat, we'd never have been the wiser. These pots would probably have stayed here another thousand years!"

Sebastian meekly limped over to his master, not realizing his glorious part in the adventure. Raymond suggested he take the shaggy discoverer home while he stood guard over the cave and its precious gifts.

When they arrived home, Sammy cleaned the cut around Sebastian's paw and put a bandage on it, then tucked him into his basket so he could rest. As soon as the adventure-weary dog fell asleep, Sammy grabbed a sandwich for himself and rushed back to the cave.

When he entered, he heard Uncle Raymond, Abu Hanna, Artine and Clovis all chorus, "Here he is — our young archaeologist!"

Clovis said warmly, "You're timing is perfect! We're just about to discuss the finds."

Artine, with great precision, had already started to identify the various periods represented by the vessels. "Aha! These are Late Bronze Age Cypriote importations."

"You mean they were brought here from the island of Cyprus?"

"Exactly, Sammy. And back there behind Raymond is a group of Middle Bronze highly burnished red ware. And up on that ledge, beautiful Persian period torpedo-shaped storage jars, or amphora. Here is a group of Hellenistic jars; notice the stamped handles. And some Roman amphorae too. Humm. It appears the Romans were the last to have used this cave."

"But how can you tell which pots belong to which period?"

"Oh, mainly by the clay, the shape, and the decoration. It takes some study, but it is most important for the archaeologist, Sammy," chimed in Clovis.

"This whole thing seems so strange. Why should they all be here, in this one cave?" asked the young explorer.

"I'll bet the Byblites used it for provisions when they were threatened by war or some other danger."

"Over so many different periods?" Uncle Raymond asked.

"It must have been a sort of general hideaway or storeroom through the ages," declared Clovis.

The two archaeologists, in consultation with Abu Hanna, planned their course of action. Sammy already knew that, in order not to destroy the evidence, they had to be very careful. The knowledge gained from the cave and its contents could be passed on to scholars of today and far into the future only if the greatest accuracy was used to record all its details. The exact placement and the position of everything in the cave had to be painstakingly drawn and photographed. Otherwise the cave's precious information would be lost forever.

After a little while, a group of men appeared at the entrance. One young man carried surveying equipment, another drafting. Artine and Clovis told them what to do. The draftsman was also laden down with cameras. With the aid of a flash, he took a series of photos of the cave and then all of its contents. Meanwhile, Clovis and Artine had started to describe each pot on individual field slips. No one had touched any part of the evidence — except Sebastian, of course, and even the debris that broke over his head was recorded with care.

"Well, this is how you begin to do all of this!" Sammy felt overwhelmed.

"We began by naming it. We called it S.B.C. 35, which mean's 'Sea Byblos Cave' and '35' is its exact location in relation to the over-all site survey stations." Artine joined in, "Now we must describe each pot in relation to its position in the Cave S.B.C. 35. First we write up this amphora resting against the north wall."

"Isn't it confusing? How can you tell one pot from another?" asked Sammy.

"Oh, after the cave has been fully documented, we'll print a number on the bottom of each pot. At this point we don't want to touch anything so we only describe it," explained Clovis.

"As soon as Youssef develops his pictures and completes an exact drawing of the cave, with the position of each pot, and we have assembled all the records, we can move the vessels to the excavation house for further study. Sammy, you've given us a lot of work to do." Clovis chuckled, "Well, that's our job. Thank heavens for discoveries like this or there wouldn't be any archaeology!"

Artine and Clovis decided to sleep in the cave in case it might attract curious townspeople, animals or dealer-looters. The faint glow of the setting sun reminded them that night would soon be falling. While Pierre, the surveyor, stayed to gather up his equipment, the two men hurried home to pack provisions for the night. Sammy walked a little way with Clovis, reluctant to leave his friend on this momentous day. At the turn-off, he headed home. Arriving, he checked on Sebastian, and then, feeling as if he would burst with excitement, sought out Uncle Raymond.

That evening Sammy picked up his book on the Mamelukes and read, "There were two Mameluke Dynasties, the Bahri (1250-1382) and the Burji (1380-1571)." After the day he'd had, his reading seemed dull indeed.

Uncle Raymond found him and helped him with a description of Mameluke Byblos, "What a sad scene would have met you, Sammy! Was this the happy Gibelet˜ of the Crusaders? Everyone now appeared to be miserable! A series of bloody battles had taken place between the Mamelukes and the Christians. In 1289, the Sultan led his troops against Tripoli and conquered the city. The last of three battles was a bloody nightmare. Then, 30,000 Maronite Christians, plus a regiment of Crusaders, attacked the Mamelukes, and in a surprise ambush,

succeeded in killing almost all of them. After the battle, the Christians formed a gruesome pyramid of Mameluke skulls. The Mamelukes had an inferior form of government and there was a drought which led to a famine, which then led to a plague. Then, if that wasn't bad enough, as if to cleanse the earth, an earthquake broke."

"Some years later the Mamelukes reinforced themselves and they, in turn, annihilated a Christian army of 150,000! After that, they settled themselves in Byblos and the surrounding area of north Lebanon."

Sammy felt suffocated. What a terrible period. After he said goodnight to Uncle Raymond, he went to visit Sebastian. "Poor dog," he said, but he really meant poor everybody.

His thoughts strayed to Artine and Clovis guarding the treasure and wished he could have stayed with them. After whispering a good night to Sebastian, he went to bed. "How I would have liked to sleep in the cave!" he grumbled to himself. After all, it was *his* discovery! Shortly, he fell asleep.

'Sea Byblos Cave 35' undergoing excavation

CHAPTER 16 — Excavation

Under Turkish Control
1516-1840

Early that Friday morning, Clovis burst into Sammy's bedroom. As if in a dream, Sammy listened to Clovis. He was half-dazed; Clovis had wakened him and it was only 6:00 a.m. He felt, more than heard, Clovis' anger mounting. The thieves had been looting again, five days since 'the gang' had made their discovery of coins.

Clovis was wildly pacing the room, waving his arms while he spoke excitedly. "I had to tell you before anyone else, Sammy. We caught the traitors! Now we need you to identify the large man you saw. Let me start at the beginning. Are you awake?"

"Sure, sure, Clovis, go on!"

"Our police chief is no fool. The thieving had to be stopped. It was as simple as that. He wanted to act immediately last Sunday, but had to wait for instructions from Beirut. Nothing could be left to chance. Meanwhile, 'the gang's' story was checked out and the cave was put under constant watch. It was searched on Monday. Not only were there artifacts, but also a ledger and precisely-drawn maps showing different points on the site. Furthermore, there were other maps indicating that stolen artifacts were buried in the mountains. The police checked those points on Tuesday and Wednesday, and it was discovered that the earth had been freshly turned. Until last night, nothing was done. The police didn't want the criminals to know that they were under suspicion.

"Intelligence reports from the cave indicated that there was more than one person involved. On the shore, there were distinct shoe marks of two

people — one large and the other a small person with the footprints the size of a boy's or girl's. There may be more people involved than that because it seems to be a large operation. Of course that is what I had thought all the time. No one could have looted the site without some knowledge of the guards' movements. I knew that it must be an inside job. Yes, I knew it, but I'm getting ahead of the story. So, once the go-ahead came, we, along with two agents from Beirut, surrounded the area. This operation was not expected to be simple. We knew that we might be up against professionals and that they might carry their own protection."

"Guns?"

"Exactly. Our chief wanted to capture them without gunfire. We had to take them by surprise. We couldn't hide in the cave because there was no way out should our movements have been spotted. So last evening, one group positioned itself in a nearby cave and the other concealed itself behind rocks in sight of the main cave. We waited and watched for what seemed to be an eternity. The sun was going down, it was going to be dark soon. Finally, a trawler came into view and proceeded towards the shore. Once it was moored, a man disembarked and started walking to the cave. The chief, who had been crouching behind a stone near the entrance, sprang on top of the man, and knocked him to the ground. A wild struggle took place. Finally, the chief hit him on the head with his gun. Bewildered,

confused and angry, the thief lapsed into wild abuses.

"Clovis, what did you do?"

"I froze, Sammy. I held the flashlight up to his face and screamed, 'You, you of all people! How can it be?'"

"Who was it?"

"Abu Hanna!"

"Abu Hanna? I don't understand. Why did he do it?"

"Blackmail, I guess. His brother was deep in gambling debts, and his life was threatened. He begged for mercy and confessed immediately — the man behind the scenes is a dealer named Hess. That's all he could tell us."

"But Clovis, it wasn't Abu Hanna that I saw digging!"

"I know. Abu Hanna was waiting for someone else, the large man you described. We reasoned that this man might be on his way to the cave. Anyway, we bound Abu Hanna and hid him. At about two in the morning, we heard the approach of a car coming across the fields above the caves. As the driver opened the Land Rover door, he was grabbed before he knew what was happening, and I fired two shots in the air to signal the capture. I had never seen him before. His eyes were full of hatred. We overpowered him and he lost control. It was awful — grunts of fury, biting, twisting and kicking, and he kept shouting abuses at Abu Hanna. It took three of us to hold him down in the Land Rover. We collected Abu Hanna and moved them both to the police station, arriving only about an hour ago. They were locked up and the police just finished questioning them. I came here right after we filed the police report."

"If we have you as a witness, I am sure we will get a confession. Believe me, Sammy, the shock and horror of the whole thing is still here." Clovis exclaimed thumping his chest.

As Sammy dressed, Clovis continued. "Of course, we want to avoid the scandal of Abu Hanna. It does not serve the interests of the excavation to have this embarrassment. On the other hand, no sympathy is going to be shown to the thief. If you can identify his accomplice, they will both be taken to prison in Beirut."

Sammy put on his red shirt, now worn thin. With his air of being askew, and in a state of shock, he walked into the police station with Clovis. Half-crazed, the burly man was brought in for the final test. Sammy identified the criminal. And with that, everything fell into place, except for his feelings about Abu Hanna. Those would take him a long time to work on.

They would find the crates and carry the finds out of the mountains. Unfortunately, the artifacts would confuse scholars in their reconstruction of the site because they were out of their context — they would take a great deal of care and time to study.

How important Sammy felt! The news of his discoveries had spread throughout Byblos — yes and all the way to Beirut. He beamed when Monsieur Dunand, Director of the excavation, congratulated him. "Mes félicitations!" he began in French. Then, "We owe you a lot."

Clovis nodded vigorously.

Sebastian thoroughly enjoyed the whole affair and he seemed to swagger as he marched about the town.

Sammy had been given special permission to watch the excavation of the cavern he had discovered, and to have the added fun of performing odd jobs for the archaeologists. It was a great honor to actually be a part of the dig, and what a wonderful way to observe the archaeologists' methods, instead of just being told about them. Day after day he learned something new. They really did measure everything carefully.

Every chance he got he wandered over to talk to Clovis or one of the other people on the team. He happened to ask Pierre, the surveyor, if this dig had any problems.

"No special problems, but different methods are used for excavating a cave than for a tell or a site with monumental architecture like a temple."

"What's a tell?" asked the ever-curious Sammy.

"It's an artificial, generally flat-topped mound which grew higher and higher because people kept building on top of past levels of occupation. It sort of looks like a huge layer cake."

"Is it harder to dig?"

"No, not necessarily. It just requires a slightly different process. Come on, I'll show you. Here, inside the cave, we've marked two points which we call *datum points*. See, the roof and the sides of the cavern form natural points for this. Between these two points we have an imaginary line, known as a *datum line*."

Sammy felt confused. Things were really getting technical. "What's a 'datum point'?"

Pierre, realizing that Sammy was struggling, explained very slowly, "It is a fixed point from which we measure. It is the basis for all our measurements, so that the finds can be plotted accurately in regard to the cave itself and in exact relationship to each other." Moving deeper into the cave, Pierre went on, "Here is the datum point, Point A." Then he moved to the side of the cave, "Here is Point B. An imaginary straight line runs between the two points. That's the datum line."

"Got it! Okay, now how do you measure?"

"Well, first we take the measurements of the object from Point A and then from Point B. This makes a triangular measurement which we can easily plot on the site plan."

"Oh, then this cave by itself is considered a site?"

Pierre nodded.

"Do you use a datum line on a tell?"

"Yes, always in excavation. If it weren't for the datum line and these fixed points, we would not have an accurate picture of the relationship of structures and finds to the site."

Sammy's mind whirled a bit. "Huh?"

Pierre tried again. "The relationship of whatever is left of *structures* — buildings, fire pits, bins, walls, and *finds*, which could be pottery, tools, weapons, jewelry, and so on. Okay?"

"I think so." Sammy concentrated very hard. Somehow he realized this was the nuts-and-bolts of archaeology, the so-called "donkey work" that made the glamorous theorizing about a past culture possible. Watching Youssef in his draftsman role, recording on graph paper the exact find-spot and numbering each object, then sketching each jar, helped him understand the actual basics of the recording. For one week, the same procedure was carried on and lots of records and photographs were amassed.

Finally, each pot was tenderly packed to be moved to the old Arabic dig house where they would be even more fully documented before being transported to the National Museum.

"Now what's going to happen, Clovis?"

"Oh, our job is far from finished here. This is merely the latest level of use in the cave."

"You mean, there may be earlier levels underneath? Older than the Middle Bronze Age pottery we found?" Sammy was amazed. He never stopped being surprised by this onion skin reality of archaeology. Maybe that is why it fascinated him so much.

"We certainly hope so. After all, we haven't reached the original floor of the cavern yet. There may be much more to uncover." With that fascinating statement dropped into Sammy's mind, Clovis walked with the two of them — they were the last ones there — to the entrance and locked the newly-erected wooden door that would protect the site and its contents from thieves.

That evening at dinner, Aunt Nadia announced that she must schedule Sammy's return to Boston. The boy had dreaded this moment. He was so involved now, he wanted never to leave. He fought back his feelings as best he could, and as soon as possible escaped down to the shore to walk with Sebastian in the Mediterranean dusk — just the two of them.

"Oh, Sebastian, how can I leave you behind, too?" Suddenly he felt overcome with loneliness. He knew that part of him would always belong to Byblos. This was HIS town! He felt sick. Only about a week left to stay. Slowly he realized this was no way to enjoy that week. Sammy threw back his shoul-

ders and resolved to capture every minute.

Much later, in the stillness of the night, he sneaked out with Sebastian and took a moonlit stroll. How dream-like the ruins appeared.

"Time, time, time! I need more time to dream, to talk, yes, and to learn. Why is life so difficult? Adults sometimes complicate our lives," he cried silently to the moon.

Sammy hardly allowed Clovis out of his sight. The archaeologist understood all too well how the boy felt. He was so fond of him that he felt pretty dismal, too. He understood Sammy's desperate wanting to learn more, and he spent as much time with him as possible.

He even went with Clovis to buy his groceries — a five minute walk from the site, through the Castle Square, under the Crusader East Gate, down the arcaded *souk*, past the police station or 'gendarmerie' where the old town ended and the new town began. Sebastian tagged along as the two discussed the best way for Sammy to finish his study of Byblos.

"Take me back into history, Clovis," the boy pleaded, feeling a bit frantic about it all.

"All right. Tell me, what do you know about the Turks?"

"They were also known as the Otto.. Otto... mmm, what was that name again?" asked Sammy.

"Ha, ha! No, not the Ottommms, Sammy. You mean the 'Ottomans'! But seriously, the Ottomans were Turks of Mongol origin, who defeated the Mamelukes in 1517 and took over."

"But what happened to the Mamelukes? Did they just disappear into thin air?"

"Oh, no. Sultan Selim I, the Ottoman leader, allowed the Mamelukes to serve in the Turkish army, and they became powerful once again at a later time. So powerful, in fact, that much later, at the end of the eighteenth century, they fought against Napoleon when he invaded Egypt."

"Who won?"

"Napoleon did for a while, but that gets complicated, too. The British got into the war and defeated Napoleon at sea."

After Clovis had done his shopping and the three started home, laden down with packages, Sammy persisted. "Let's get back to the Ottoman Turks. Now, can you tell me what happened after they defeated the Mamelukes?"

"Well, when the Turkish army invaded Cairo, it had much more advanced weapons than had the Mamelukes."

"Same old story," said Sammy with a sigh, remembering the Amorite attack on the city.

"In 1516, the Turks fought a full-scale battle in Syria and won with a complete victory. One year later they marched into Cairo, then took over Egypt and Lebanon as well as the rest of the Near East."

"How did the Byblites take to their new overlords?"

"It is said that Sultan Selim I governed Byblos peacefully."

"Well, that's good to hear, after what happened under the Mamelukes. How long did the Turks rule?"

"The Ottoman Empire dominated Lebanon for over four-hundred years."

"Four-hundred years!"

But the citizens of Byblos, as well as the people of other Lebanese towns, had suffered under a group known as the *Sayfas* who treated them with cruelty. Prince Fakhreddin, ruler of Byblos and Emir of Lebanon, had been exiled to Italy between 1613 and 1618. He had been forced out in dishonor, but five years later, he made a triumphal return. The people joyously welcomed him.

As they came to the arcaded *souk*, Clovis said, "By the way, Sammy, this *souk* you have been running up and down all summer was built by the Ottomans. We think that it was outside the earlier Medieval town. There isn't much remaining from the

Turkish period except for some old houses, like your Aunt Nadia's!"

Sammy couldn't believe that he had been living in a 'Turkish house' all along, and had never known it.

Since Clovis had been invited for dinner, they had a chance to talk briefly about the Turkish period. The archaeologist told him that the whole area had enjoyed peace and security as a result of the Prince's able rule. "And you know, the Chehab family, who were related to Fakhreddin, came from here. Later in the 18th century the Turks allowed them to rule over the independent principality of Mount Lebanon, the central Christian mountain province of our country."

Roaming through the quiet Byblos of the Ottoman period, Sammy noticed that the town had not undergone any dramatic architectural changes from the Crusader-Mameluke times.

Later that evening, as the boy sat on his little balcony — the air filled with the sweet scent of jasmine and the mad din of cicadas, he wondered if the archaeologists really understood the people who had stored their pots in the cave. "What is the truth?" He pondered that question for some time.

Sammy helps Uncle Raymond with his fishing tackle and a successful catch in Byblos port

CHAPTER 17

A Final Look

Modern Byblos
1840-Present

When Sammy's birthday arrived on September second, he felt miserable. First, tomorrow was his scheduled departure from Lebanon — from HIS Byblos, and from his Sebastian. Only hours left. And second, he was angry with himself because he had left his picture-taking to the last minute.

"I can't believe it! Oh, Sebastian, what can I do?" he moaned, throwing a stick for the dog.

When the four-legged one returned with the stick, he ,at least, had a brighter look in his eye, as if to say, "Throw it again! Things aren't all that bad."

Sammy scuffed along, ignoring the stick. "This is one of the last walks we'll be able to take together," he whispered as he patted his shaggy friend.

Sebastian was beginning to feel something was definitely wrong. His master was so mopey.

As Sammy stood on the Crusader wall photographing the ruins from the castle, a familiar figure in a safari hat, waving madly, popped into his viewfinder. "Hey, Sammy! Don't you want a picture of me?"

"Clovis! Of course I do! Stay right where you are."

Clovis assumed a formal pose, very dignified, with a very serious expression.

"Smile! You look like a statue, and not a very good one at that!" Sammy teased.

The archaeologist broke into a broad grin, relaxing his taut shoulders, and Sammy snapped the picture. Moments later, Clovis joined him on the top of the keep.

125

"Can you tell me something about those old cannon balls sticking out of these walls?" Sammy asked.

Clovis happily responded. "Cannons of the British fleet bombarded the town in 1840, and ever since then the balls have been lodged where they landed — in the castle walls. There are even some in the walls of both the Byzantine and Crusader Churches!"

"But why the British?" Sammy felt definitely confused by that one.

"Well, the British were allied with the Turks then," Clovis explained, "and the Turks wanted to regain their hold over the Eastern Mediterranean, which at that time was being defended by both Egyptian and Lebanese forces. When the British opened fire on Byblos, the garrison stationed in the Castle replied as best they could with antique cannons, and stood their ground! The British shelled everything in sight, including the Cathedral. That's when the front of the Crusader Church was blasted away. The story goes that when the parishioners of the Byzantine chapel saw that the church was being hit, they acted fast and positioned a huge wooden cross on the chapel roof. The cross was seen by the British and they directed their fire to the Castle and St. John's Crusader Church."

"Did they land?"

"No, we successfully defended and they sailed away!"

"Then what happened?"

"It gets very complicated. Political shenanigans, a dissident Lebanese group, the withdrawal of the defending Egyptian troops to the mountains — in short, the British landed a month later."

"Did that bring peace?"

"No!" Clovis was getting excited. "It gets worse. The dissident Lebanese group was put into power, and then yanked out of power, by the British and Turks. This country of Lebanon — imagine Sammy, is only the size of your state of Connecticut — divided against itself, and civil war erupted in 1860. The Europeans intervened and established a Christian governor who ruled from 1861 to 1914. The French temporarily occupied Lebanon, then the Turks again — arbitrary Ottoman rule completely taking over until after World War I. In 1920, Lebanon was declared an autonomous state under a French Mandate. In 1926 it wrenched free and became independent and was reorganized as the Lebanese Republic. But it took until 1936-1937 and a treaty with France for its Constitution to be restored. Then it was under the control of the Vichy French in 1940, and in 1941 it was passed on to the British and the Free French. Again it was declared independent on the date all of us remember: November 22, 1943."

"Finally Lebanon was free."

"No, not entirely. The French didn't evacuate their troops until 1946. Only then was Lebanon free.

Yes, Sammy, I'm afraid we've known our share of feuding, war, and domination by stronger powers. In 1948-49, Lebanon played a small role in the Arab-Israeli War, and in 1958 our government asked U.S. troops to come to Lebanon when we were about to start a civil war."

"What happened in Byblos?"

"Here, we were removed from most of these problems. Even today we, Byblites, go along in our sleepy, quiet way, pretending and hoping that things will be better tomorrow."

"Well, how about the French? Were they interested in Byblos?"

"How odd that you asked. It was during the first period of their 'protection,' in about 1860, that a great archaeologist named Ernest Renan was sent by Napoleon III on a 'Mission to Phoenicia.' Renan spent some time here and realized how essential it was to excavate. He is now regarded as the father of Byblos archaeology." Clovis continued, waving a dramatic finger, "The French Emperor, Napoleon III, issued an imperial decree ordering a survey of Byblos and neighboring sites. But it wasn't until the 1920's that the Lebanese Department of Antiquities was founded, and Monsieur Dunand was appointed the Director of excavations just shortly thereafter."

"Then he's dedicated his entire life to the dig."

Clovis nodded, motioning toward the site. "Yes, Byblos reflects his genius. And it is here, in this now so-small town, that we can really appreciate the history of our people."

Sammy was thoughtful as he took in the commanding view of the ruins and beyond, the sea. Then, glancing down from the wall, he noticed Monsieur Dunand himself strolling across the Early Bronze Age Baalat Gebal and Reshef temple area.

"What are you looking at so intently?"

"It's Monsieur Dunand with another man."

Following Sammy's line of sight, Clovis said, "The other person is Emir Maurice Chehab, Director of the Lebanese Department of Antiquities in Beirut."

"'Chehab' is a Byblos name?"

"In the 17th century, they were the ruling dynasty of Byblos, and have been several times since. During the Ottoman period, the Turks, along with the English, even appointed Bashir Chehab ruler of all of Lebanon — then they turned around in 1841 and toppled him. Actually, the Chehabs were our last native ruling family. The 'Emir,' meaning native ruler or prince, walking over there, is a direct descendant."

Sebastian was getting restless. Too much talk and too little play. Sammy sensed it and said, "I haven't taken pictures of the north port yet, Clovis. Can you come with us?"

"Sure, let's go!" The archaeologist had especially requested the afternoon off so he could spend these last hours with this wonderfully eager boy.

After eating at Tewfik's, the two-plus-dog followed the beautiful and scenic street pattern of Medieval Byblos and went directly down the hill to the column-choked port. Sammy photographed the half-ruined north tower with its stones of varying periods, plus cut-off Roman columns.

"Boy, the Crusaders used anything they could to build. Look at those parts of Roman columns stuck in the water?"

Clovis nodded, "See over there, just above the water line? Stuck in between those stones? Believe it or not, that's part of a carved limestone sarcophagus of the Roman period."

The once fortified defenses of the city were now only scattered traces of their past glory. Then, being a hardy explorer, Sammy climbed the north port tower to get a view of the town. The inspiring panorama of Byblos was too much for a single picture, but he did manage to capture the walls of the Genoese storehouses, the city walls, the church and modern Byblos' fishing fleet.

Sammy carefully put down his camera and climbed around the base of the tower to have a better look. Balanced precariously on a building block, he was startled by a loud close horn. It jolted him. "Help! I'm falling into the soup!"

SPLASH!

An instant later Sammy bobbed up on the surface. "What in the...!"

Clovis was laughing wildly. Instinctively Sammy turned his head and saw what looked to him to be Pepé's huge yacht — and at the rail, laughing riotously, was Uncle Raymond.

"There should be a law against sneaking up behind a guy and blowing that maddening fog horn! Look at me — I'm drenched!"

Uncle Raymond could hardly speak. Between spasms of laughter he managed to get out, "Swim over here and we'll help you get out."

As Sammy climbed up the ladder, and onto the boat, Uncle Raymond handed him a big towel. "You look like a drowned rat, my boy!" And then Pepé too collapsed in laughter. Sammy was somewhere between feeling ridiculous and furious. He had always admired Uncle Raymond's special sense of humor and warmth, so he decided the best course of action was to laugh at himself.

After a special boat ride up the coast, Sammy thanked Pepé. It had been wonderful.

When they docked, Sebastian was waiting, tail wagging, to greet them. As they left the port, troubled Sammy, said to Clovis and Uncle Raymond both, "Will you please take care of Sebastian after I leave?"

"Don't worry, Sammy, we'll be sure that he's taken care of," Clovis vowed.

Uncle Raymond smiled kindly, "He can always go fishing with me! You won't need to worry about him."

With Clovis, Uncle Raymond, and Sebastian,

Sammy walked up the sloping path to the sleepy town. In the square, they checked in at Tewfik's to see what was going on. While Sammy sipped a juice, Tewfik put two Lebanese-costumed dolls on the table. "Take these to your sister Nina — and here's a little something for you to remember me by."

As Sammy opened the 'little something,' Tewfik said, "I hope you will return to visit us some day. You are always welcome."

To Sammy's utter joy, he had been given a *kaffiyeh*, or Arab headdress. He was so moved he hardly knew what to say. He sputtered out, "Thanks, Tewfik, for everything."

Clovis showed Sammy how to fold it, and fixed it on his head, "Now you look like Lawrence of Arabia!"

Clutching the gifts, he rushed over to the storeroom to find Artine, Youssef, and the others. Sadly he looked at Abu Hanna's empty place. They spoke of next year — when Sammy would return. They said good-bye, but meant "We shall meet again."

He then went to the site for a last look. He and Sebastian made their way over to the Castle, and next walked down into the temple area and snapped a last photo of the Temple of the Obelisks. Then, wandering over to the spring, he thought, "Without this fresh water, there would probably have been no Byblos."

From the Bronze Age Palace the boy and his dog went to the Neolithic plastered-floor area, and pausing by the bluff, Sammy looked out to sea just as those long-ago people must have. He glanced up at the Arabic excavation house, halted at the jar burial, and then climbed the hill to the Temple of Balaat Gebal. Slowly he ambled over to the Phoenician-period royal tombs, and then stopped for a farewell look at the small Roman theater.

With Sebastian following at his heels, he ran down into the plateau and up into the castle — up the winding steps of the keep, to his secret room.

129

Looking out over the site, spread like a panorama before him, all the pent-up emotion he had so bravely been holding back spilled out. Nearly blinded with tears, he bent down to move the heavy stone from the secret hiding place where he had kept his book and art materials. There was a little box in the hole! What's this? Who knew about my secret place? He opened it. Inside was a note which said, "Keep me always and I will bring you luck!" Underneath was a coin, a beautiful Arabic silver coin. Sammy was thrilled! It must have been Clovis.

Smiling happily now, the boy dried his eyes on his faded red shirt sleeve. He decided to take one last look around the old town — the *souk*, the shops. He would visit the 'gang,' and then go home to pack. He and Sebastian bounded down the stairs, walking into the *souk* area where he stopped to say good-bye to each of his *souk* shopkeeper friends, especially blind Assad. Every one of them wanted to give him a small treasure, a remembrance of his stay. Sammy had to work hard all over again at controlling himself. Before the blacksmith's shop, where the street bent, Sammy looked back at the aged two-story shops which made up the charming old street. After he said his good-byes to Wasfi, Jamil and Hamid, he quickly took off for home, the house he felt was home.

Laden with gifts stowed in the string bag Assad had kindly given him, he arrived home just in time to pack before a big family farewell party — plus Clovis, of course!

By dinner time his suitcase was ready. He wanted to turn over to the government most of his panned sherds-from-the-sea and beach collection. Clovis, as the government representative, spent some time going over the collection and his catalog with Sammy. Some of the things, the archaeologist told him, he could keep, but he felt that they shouldn't leave the country; they would really be out of context in Boston! Aunt Nadia assured him she would take care of the collection until he could once again visit them. Clovis suggested that he take one glass and one pottery fragment. He decided to carry on the plane his fragile treasure, the modern Roman lamp for Nina and the precious Phoenician ship in a bag specially packed to keep them from breaking.

That evening was spent in feasting and merriment. The table was laden with all the foods he had come to love; *kibbé*, mountain bread, *hommos*, *schawarma*, to name just a few. His aunt ran to and fro, bringing platters of food, until laden dishes covered the snowy tablecloth. As soon as Sammy had stuffed a last delectable *kibbé* into his mouth, he snuck off to give one to Sebastian.

At last, the family quieted down so Uncle Raymond could sing a farewell blessing in Syriac. Clovis whispered that Syriac was similar to the language spoken by Christ. It was more ancient than

Arabic and was barely used now except by the Maronite clergy in Byblos.

Then it was time for bed and Sammy gave each a fond good-bye hug.

Thus, quietly in the dawn of September third, Sammy gave his biggest hug to dear Sebastian, his true companion. "Be good, pal. Stay away from cats and go to Clovis and Uncle Raymond for care." Holding the dog's head in his hands, he vowed to return to Byblos. "I'll come back, old buddy, my Sebastian. I am at home here. I have it in my blood. I am part of Byblos." He couldn't say any more, but gave another hug to the shaggy mongrel, a last, long hug.

"Got everything in the car?" called Clovis.

Uncle Raymond, Clovis and Aunt Nadia accompanied Sammy to Beirut International Airport. The boy savored his last wild ride down the coast — it appealed to his senses. He loved the Lebanese — they were happy to be alive and they radiated that feeling.

He boarded the jumbo jet for Boston. The plane's door was shut. They taxied down the runway, and the craft lifted into the air and headed out to sea — his beautiful Mediterranean sea, glistening its own farewell in the morning light.

* * *

To old Byblos Sammy had brought a special quality — his wondering, questing, searching mind. It was like discovering something that had always been a part of him — a hunch or intuition — to know the ruins, the lay of the land, the people, the spirit. It had directly pointed into his heart.

If you too are looking for a special feeling — an ecstatic experience, outside anything you have ever known, or if you just want to drop by for a visit, you may find Clovis, Uncle Raymond, Aunt Nadia, Pepé, Tewfik, 'the gang' and others who loved the boy. And of course, Sebastian. Look out for them, they will always be there!

**Chronological list
of Princes
and Kings of Byblos**

Amorite rulers 2300-1800 B.C.

Abishemu I
Ypshemuabi
Ib-dadi
Inten

Egyptian Protectorate 16th - 13th Centuries B.C.

Rib-Addi
Rabimur (?)
Abishemou II

Independent Byblos 13th - 8th Centuries B.C.

Abishou II
Zakar-Baal
Yehowmilk I
Ahiram
Itobaal
Yehowmilk II
Abibaal
Ozbaal
Elibaal
Shipitbaal

Assyro-Babylonian domination 6th - 4th Centuries B.C.

Yarhabaal
Yakhawmilk
El-Pa'al
Azbaal
Adramelek
Ayinal

Glossary

To those who wish to know more
about some of the terms used in this book.
It offers a brief explanation for those who may be having
their first contact with Byblos.

A

Abishemu — A king of Byblos during the Middle Bronze Age 1900-1600 B.C. His sarcophagus can be seen at Byblos lying in its underground shaft tomb.

Acropolis — The upper part of a city, one that stands on a natural rock outcrop and is generally fortified, such as the Acropolis of Athens.

A.D. — Abbreviation meaning Anno Domini, or after Christ.

Adonis — A handsome young man who fell in love with Venus (or Aphrodite); a valley and river in Lebanon near Byblos bear his name.

Agora — The ancient Greek word for the market place; a meeting place. During ancient times, the agora was not only the center for buying and selling, but also the principal gathering place, meeting place — for politics, entertainment, or just a sociable stroll.

Ahiram — A King of Byblos. His stone sarcophagus is dated to about 1200 B.C., and bears one of the earliest Phoenician inscriptions found at Byblos. It is carved with a lotus design (Egyptian in origin) and lions which are said to be Hittite in origin. The tomb was discovered by archaeologists in 1924.

Ahlan — An Arabic greeting meaning "welcome."

Ahlan wa salan — An Arabic greeting meaning, "You are especially welcome."

Akkadian — One of the Semitic languages or cultures of Mesopotamia.

Alabaster — A white, translucent, sometimes striped stone that was often carved into vases.

Alexander the Great — 356-323 B.C. The son of Philip of Macedon. He conquered the eastern Mediterranean world and Asian territories extending as far east as India. These conquests were responsible for the spread of Greek culture. Also see Hellenistic.

Allah — The Supreme Being of the Muslim religion, the Arabic name for God.

Alphabet — The letters of a language written in symbols representing a single sound and ordered by custom.

Amphora (amphorae pl.) — An ancient Greek storage jar with two handles and a narrow neck, used to store oil or wine.

Amorite — Semitic nomads who moved to Byblos about 2300 B.C. and ruled until about 1900 B.C. They are thought to have come from North Syria — they spread south and east into Lower Mesopotamia and west into the Lebanon-Palestine area. All the rulers of Byblos in the Middle Bronze Age have Amorite or Semitic names.

Apse — A semi-circular projection of a church, usually domed.

Arab — A Semitic people of the Near East and North Africa.

Arabic bread — Large loaves of flat pocket bread, like pita bread. Mountain bread has no pockets, is flat and thin like paper.

Archaeologist — A specialist trained to excavate, study, interpret and publish the remains of an ancient culture.

Aristotle — A Greek philosopher who lived between 384 and 322 B.C.

Artifact — An object made or altered by man.

Assyria — An ancient empire (900-612 B.C.) of Mesopotamia in western Asia that extended along the Tigris River to the East.

Astarte — The Phoenician moon goddess, who was also the goddess of love.

Astrolobe — An instrument used to determine the altitude of the stars.

134

B

Baal — "Lord," a local god of the Byblites and the most important god of the Canaanites, God of storms, rain. Son of the sky god, El, whom he replaced as chief god of the Semite pantheon. As bringer of nourishing rain, he is also a fertility god. He is usually represented as a young, armed warrior wearing a helmet with bull's horns.

Baalat Gebal — 'The Lady of Byblos', the fertility and nature goddess of Byblos. She was associated with the Egyptian goddess, Hathor (the Cow goddess), who was the goddess of women and childbirth. She appears in art wearing the solar disc between cow's horns on her head as the Egyptian goddess Isis.

Babylon — The ancient capital of Babylonia and Mesopotamia.

Babylonia — An ancient empire in Mesopotamia.

Bahri — A Mameluke Dynasty of 1250-1390 A.D.

Banu Ammar — The Emir of Tripoli during the First Arab period.

Basilica — An oblong building which was used in the Roman period as a court or place of assembly. Such buildings were later used as Christian churches.

Baths — A building complex containing a series of rooms designated for bathing. The Romans were famous for their baths which were usually free and open to the public. The bathing rooms included a frigidarium (a cold water room), a tepidarium (warm water room), and a caldarium (a hot water room).

Batroun — A town north of Byblos (65 km. north of Beirut) with a Crusader Chapel; it is the main coastal city between Byblos and Tripoli.

Battering ram — A military machine with a large swinging wooden beam tipped with an iron head, used to beat down walls.

B.C. — An abbreviation meaning "Before Christ."

Beirut — The modern capital city of Lebanon.

Bohemond — A Frankish anarchist family. The Bohemond V to VII were Counts of the House of Antioch. This family ruled the city of Tripoli as a Republic in 1288 A.D.

Bronze — An alloy of copper and tin.

Bronze Age — A cultural period dating from about 3000-1200 B.C., characterized by the use of bronze tools. The period is subdivided into three stages: Early Bronze, Middle Bronze, and Late Bronze.

Bukra — An Arabic word meaning "tomorrow."

Burin — A prehistoric tool with a beveled point, generally made of flint.

Burji — A Mameluke Dynasty of 1390-1517 A.D.

Byblites — The inhabitants of Byblos.

Byblos — A Greek word meaning "papyrus", and the name given to the site on the north coast of Lebanon.

Byzantine — Relating to the city of Byzantium (Constantinople, modern Istanbul), hence the name, where the style of architecture featured the dome decorated with colored mosaics. The Byzantine period at Byblos extended from 330 A.D. to the first Arab period beginning in 636 A.D.

C

Cadiz — An important transshipment point in Spain for the metals but particularly the tin of Britain, more sought after than the easily obtained copper.

Cairo — The modern capital city of Egypt; the ancient city of Captos.

Caldarium — Steam or hot water room in a Roman bath.

Caliph — The head of Islam, a successor of Mohammad.

Cambyses — Son of Cyrus II, Cyrus the Great, King who ruled Persia from 529 to 522 B.C. and carried out his father's dream of conquering Egypt.

Canaanite — 'Low landers,' Semitic speaking peoples who lived on the Eastern Mediterranean coast during the Bronze Age. The word derives from *Kinakhnu,* or purple dye extracted from the spiny *Murex.*
(See also Phoenician).

Caracalla — A Roman emperor (188-217 A.D.) who ruled from 211 to 217 A.D.

Carnelian — A quartzite stone, generally red in color and waxy to touch.

Carthage — A 8th century B.C. trading post of Tyre. It became not only more important than the mother city, but until its defeat and eventual destruction by Rome in the Punic Wars, was known as the Mistress of the Mediterranean.

Caucasus — The mountains in the U.S.S.R between the Black and Caspian Seas.

Cedar — A long-lived evergreen tree that was traded by the Byblites for 3000 years. Once vast cedar forests covered the hills behind Byblos. These fragrant and durable trees were prized by the Egyptians who used them for their solar boats, coffins and mummification.

Chalcolithic — Derived from the Greek meaning "copper-stone." The period that follows the Neolithic at Byblos which dates from 4000 to 3000 B.C. It is succeeded by the Bronze Age. It refers to the period when stone and the first metal objects were both in use as tools.

Chancel — The part of a church containing the altar, seats for the priests and the choir. It is generally separated from the rest of the church by a latticework screen.

Chehab — A ruling family in Lebanon. One of its descendants is the Emir Maurice Chehab, the former Director of Antiquities, Republic of Lebanon.

Chipped stone — A stone that has been chipped or knapped to create a core, flake or blade tool. The chipping process leaves scars that vary in size and shape.

Chiton — The flowing garment of the ancient Greeks. Men wore it knee-length and women full-length.

Christianity — The religion based on the teachings of Jesus Christ that considers the Bible sacred; it is professed by Eastern, Roman Catholic, Maronite, and Protestant churches.

Cicadas — The family of insects that includes the grasshopper.

Coinage — To convert metal into something of a specific value that is generally issued by a government authority. Coinage is thought to have been first invented at Sardis (the capital of Lydia in Asia Minor) in the 7th century B.C. The practice spread rapidly throughout the civilized world.

Composite bow — An offensive weapon made up of distinct parts which allow for greater flexibility and a longer shooting distance.

Constantine the Great — The Roman Emperor from 306 to 337 A.D. who transferred the capital of the Roman Empire from Rome to Constantinople, and made Christianity the official religion of the Empire.

Constantinople — Byzantium, modern Istanbul in Turkey; the capital of the late Roman Empire.

Crusaders — The military men who took part in the Christian expeditions to the Holy Land from the 11th to the 13th centuries A.D. Their purpose was to win the Holy Land from the Muslims.

Crusades — The campaigns of the Crusaders.

Cuneiform — A script of wedge-shaped characters, developed and used by the people of Mesopotamia, Syria and other Near Eastern countries.

Cylinder seal — A seal, usually made of stone, with symbols carved on the outside of the cylinder which leave an impression when rolled on wet clay.

Cyprus — An island in the Eastern Mediterranean Sea which lies to the south of Turkey and west of Byblos. The Latin word *cyprium* means copper.

Cyrus the Great — Also known as Cyrus II, King of Persia, who ruled between 550 and 529 B.C. A great military conqueror.

D

Damascus — The capital of modern Syria.

Daric — An ancient Persian small gold coin.

Darius — Darius I, King of Persia from 521 to 486 B.C.

Datum line — An imaginary line which is measured north-south over a site to be excavated. It serves as a fixed line of reference for the excavation.

Datum point — A permanently fixed point that serves as a reference point on an archaeological site from which all measurements are taken during an excavation.

Debké — An Arab folk dance.

Discus — A stone disk weighing about 4 pounds; it is thicker in the middle than at the edges; it is thrown for a measured distance in the Olympic games.

Donjon — The massive inner tower in a medieval castle, the keep.

Dorade — A fish commonly found in the Mediterranean Sea that resembles the salmon in shape and is delicious to eat.

Draftsman — The person on an archaeological team who works closely with the surveyor and the architect, and prepares the drawings of site plans and artifacts for final publication.

Dunand, Maurice — The French archaeologist who had excavated Byblos for the Lebanese Republic since 1926. He published many articles and volumes on Byblos including *Fouilles de Byblos I and II*. Unfortunately, he passed away in 1987.

E

Early Bronze Age — The time of high civilization throughout the Eastern Mediterranean and Mesopotamian areas. A time of the beginning of cities with palaces, temples, international trade, and the beginning of writing in the form of hieroglyphs in Egypt or cuneiform in Mesopotamia.

El — The father of the Semitic gods, claimed as the founder of Byblos. In Greek mythology, El is equated with Kronos.

Embriaci — The lords of Jebail from 1103 to 1299 A.D. who maintained rule over Byblos for nearly 200 years. They originated from the Italian city of Genoa.

Emir — The title given to a native ruler of a Middle Eastern country.

Empire — A major political unit holding authority over a large territory, generally an emperor is the head of this political unit.

Esarhaddon — King of Assyria from 681 to 669 B.C.

Euripides — A Greek playwright who lived sometime between 480 to 406 B.C. He was the last of the three great Classical Greek tragedians — the other two being Aeschylus and Sophocles. Euripides is known particularly for the emotional depth of his plays.

Excavation — The systematic and scientific digging of an archaeological site.

Excavation house — The building that serves as the base of operations for an archaeological team.

F

Fakhreddin — The Emir of Lebanon and ruler of Byblos in 1618 A.D.

Fatimid — The dynasty that ruled over North Africa between 909 and 1171 A.D.

Figurine — A small, usually carved or molded figure or statuette.

Flint — A hard quartz stone used by ancient man for making chipped stone tools such as arrowheads.

Frigidarium — The cold room in a Roman bath used for cooling off and closing the pores.

G

Galley — A large low sailing ship with oars.

Gebal — The Biblical name for Byblos.

Gibelet — The Crusader name for Byblos.

Greek — Relating to or characteristic of Greece.

Greek theater — The especially designed building where actors and the chorus would perform.

Ground stone — Stone tools that are manufactured and achieve their final form by grinding instead of chipping. Typical tools include mortars and pestles for the crushing of grain.

H

Habiru — A northern landless people who attacked Byblos in the Late Bronze Age; they finally gained control of the city from the Hyksos but were defeated by the Hittites around 1360 B.C.

Haft — To set a tool into a handle.

Hakim — An Arab word meaning "doctor", but can also mean "intelligent, bright."

Hamdillila — An Arab word meaning "praise the Lord," fine, or "all right."

Hellenistic — Relating to the period from Alexander the Great in 322 B.C. to 64 B.C. when the Roman general, Pompey, conquered the Near East. The term is derived from the Greek word "Hellas", meaning Greek. The Hellenistic period, therefore, implies the influence of Greek culture and art wherever it is found.

Helou — The Arabic word meaning "sweet", or "pretty".

Hibiscus — A plant with large red, pink or white colored flowers which grows in tropical regions.

Hieroglyphs — A picture script invented and used by the Egyptians.

Hittites — An Indo-European people who lived in Asia Minor (Turkey) and North Syria between 1900 and 1200 B.C.

Holy of Holies — The inner sanctum, *sanctum-sanctorum,* of a temple where often the image of the god was kept. An area forbidden to all but the highest priests.

Homer — A Greek epic poet thought to have been the author of *The Iliad* and *The Odyssey.*

Hommos — A soft Arab food made with chick peas, ground sesame seed oil (Tahini), garlic and lemon juice.

Hubbly-bubbly — See water pipe or nargilé.

Hyksos — Asiatic invaders who dominated Egypt from the end of the 18th century B.C. to the beginning of the 16th century B.C.

I

Infidel — A person who is not a believer in respect to a particular religion.

In situ — A term often used in archaeology meaning in the original position.

Ipshemuabi — Crown Prince of Byblos, son of Abishemu who ruled Byblos during the Middle Bronze Age.

Iron Age — A period dating from about 1200 to 530 B.C. — also known as the Phoenician period when the use of iron for tool making became widespread.

Isis — Sister and wife of the Egyptian god Osiris. In

Ptolemaic times, she became the universal goddess, the Earth mother and a supreme deity.

Islam — A religion based on the teachings of the prophet Mohammed and the belief in Allah, one supreme God.

Itfaddilou — An Arabic word meaning "welcome" or "make yourself at home."

J

Jasmine — A vine or shrub with small fragrant white or yellowish-white sweet smelling flowers.

Javelin — A light spear that is thrown, in athletic contests or in warfare, in contrast to the heavier lance or spear which are thrust.

Jebail — The modern name for Byblos.

Jerusalem — The capital of ancient Israel.

K

Kaffiyeh — A large scarf worn as a headdress by many Arabs.

Kafta — The Arab word for a dish consisting of patties made of ground lamb or beef, chopped onion and chopped parsley cooked on a grill or in the oven.

Keep — The main tower or donjon of a castle.

Kibbé — The Arab word for a dish consisting of finely ground lamb or beef mixed with cracked wheat and baked in the oven or fried. (*Kibbé Nayyeh* is eaten raw.)

Kiln — An oven or heated enclosure used for firing pottery, as opposed to more primitive techniques of open firing.

Middle English "Kiln" from Latin *"culina"* (Kitchen) from the verb *"coquere"*, meaning literally, to cook.

Kilt — A short skirt.

Koran — The sacred text of Islam containing the revelations given by Allah to Mohammed.

L

Latin — The language of ancient Rome.

Lebanon — A Republic on the East Mediterranean.

The Department of Antiquities — A section of the Lebanese government concerned with the excavation, conservation, storage and display of antiquities.

Leptis Magna — An important Roman site in northern Libya.

Levant — The countries bordering on the eastern Mediterranean coast.

Level — A horizontal volume of earth that is different from that which lies above it (unless it is the surface or ground level) and that which lies below it; it is generally distinct culturally from that which is either above or below it. A level in archaeology may also be known as a stratum.

Lingua franca — Any of various languages used at different periods of time as the commercial or common speech among peoples of diverse tongues.

M

Macrinus — A Roman emperor from 217-218 A.D. His coinage gives us an idea of what the Adonis temple of Byblos looked like.

139

Marhaba — The Arabic word meaning "hello".

Maronite — A branch of the Christian Church found chiefly in Lebanon; it has a Syriac liturgy and a married clergy but submits to papal authority.

Mars — The Roman god of war.

Marseilles — A seaport in southern France, first settled by the Phoenicians, then later, about 600 B.C., was re-founded by Greeks.

Mason's mark — The sign or symbol used by brick or stone masons to identify themselves or their workshops.

Medea — One of the principal characters in a Greek myth, who enchanted men and resorted to murder to gain her ends. She helped Jason in his quest for the Golden Fleece.

Medieval — The Middle Ages or the period from the 7th to 15th centuries A.D. At Byblos this would include the first Arab, the Crusader, and Mameluke periods.

Mes félicitations — A French expression meaning "Congratulations!"

Mesopotamia — The ancient country lying between the Tigris and the Euphrates rivers. In modern times, this area is in Iraq.

Mezzé — Appetizers or hors-d'œuvres. At a typical Byblos lunch as many as twenty separate dishes may be served.

Middle Bronze Age — The period from 1900 to 1600 B.C. and second important cultural division of the Bronze Age.

Mish quoiese — Arab words meaning "not very good."

Mohammadanism — The religion of Islam.

Mohammed — Founder and prophet of Islam who lived sometime between 570 and 632 A.D.

Mongol — A people of eastern Asia who between 1162 and 1227 were led by Genghis Khan, the conqueror.

Monotheism — The belief that there is only one God.

Mosaic — A picture or decorative design made with small inlaid colored cubes called *tesserae*, individually set in plaster or mortar. Mosaics are generally used as floor decorations. The word comes from the Latin word *"musa"*, of a muse or artistic.

Mosque — A Moslem house of worship.

Mother goddess — A revered or worshipped female, considered to be a mother figure, who cares, nourishes and protects.

Mount. Lebanon — The Lebanese Christian principality under the authority of a prince.

Mount Olympos — A lofty peak, the highest in Greece, on the northern border between Thessaly and Macedonia. The home of the Greek gods.

Mudbrick — A clay or earthen block that is unbaked, generally used as construction material.

Murex — The mussel of a spiny generally white shell that yields a purple dye. These shells were found in great beds off the coast of Lebanon and once their discovery became known, it brought fame and fortune to Phoenicia. The mollusk exudes a yellowish fluid that upon exposure to the air turns into a rich deep purple or maroon dye. This is also known as "royal purple." Today it still signifies the color of royalty.

Museum — A building which displays and stores articles of artistic, historical and scientific interest.

Muslim or Moslem — A believer in the religion of Islam.

Myth — A traditional imaginary story that tells of supernatural beings, heros, ancestors or things.

N

Nahr el-Kalb — The Dog River where rock carvings of Egyptian, Assyrian, Babylonian, Greco-Roman and other inscriptions and reliefs are found.

Napoleon III — 1808-1873, Emperor of France from 1852 to 1870 A.D.

Narghilé — An Arabic word meaning "water pipe" or hubbly-bubbly.

Narthex — The rectangular portico or vestibule of a church which leads into the nave. It stands at a right angle to the nave and runs the width of the building (its width is several times greater than its length).

Nave — The central part or rectangular hall of a church.

Necropolis — The burial ground or cemetery of an ancient city.

Nebuchadnezzar II — The Chaldean king of Babylon from 652 to 605 B.C.

Neolithic — The period of human culture beginning around 6000 B.C. and ending around 4000 B.C. at Byblos. The Neolithic period is characterized by the advent of farming, ground stone tools, and pottery.

Nubians — Inhabitants of Nubia, a region between southern Egypt and Ethiopia or north of the Sudan. From the 6th to the 14th centuries, they formed a powerful empire and ruled Egypt.

O

Obelisk — A tall, tapering four-sided pillar made of stone and usually ending in a pyramidal point.

Obelisk temple — Originally built on top of the Early Bronze Age temple (but it was moved to a new site by the archaeologists at Byblos). It is dated to 1800 B.C. and is well-preserved with steps, lower walls, and an altar. It contained a mass of votive obelisks and ships' anchors.

Olympia — A great sanctuary, dedicated to Zeus, situated in the western Peloponnesus in Greece.

Olympic games — Greek festivals of athletic competition begun in 776 B.C. These were considered so important by the Greeks that a whole year of truce would be declared — no warfare was allowed to interrupt participation.

Orchestra — The round center of the Classical theater where actors and chorus would perform.

Orthodox — Belonging to Christian Churches derived from the Church of the Byzantine Empire.

Osiris — An Egyptian god of the dead and husband of Isis.

Ottoman — Of or relating to the Turks of Turkey.

P

Palaeolithic — A period in the Stone Age characterized by the invention of chipped stone tools.

Palaestra — A square, open-air sports ground that is surrounded by a wall.

Pan — The Greek god of shepherds and hunters who is credited with the invention of the panpipe.

Papyrus — Paper made from the pulp or stem of this tall, grass-like water plant of the same name. Invented and used by the Egyptians.

Pentathlon — An athletic contest involving the contestant's participation in five (penta) different events. The modern pentathlon includes the 300 meter freestyle swim, the 4000 meter cross-country run, a 5000 meter 30 jump equestrian steeplechase, fencing, and target shooting at 25 meters.

Peplos — A piece of clothing worn by women in Ancient Greece, consisting of a rectangular cloth folded and draped on the upper body and clasped with a brooch at the shoulder.

Persia — The former name for Iran.

Persian — A native or inhabitant of Persia.

Pharaoh — A king of ancient Egypt.

Phoenician — The seafarers and merchants of the Iron Age that originated in cities of the eastern Mediterranean and settled colonies in the western Mediterranean. This term is lovingly, but incorrectly used by modern Byblites for all the civilizations in Byblos before the Greco-Roman period (i.e., Semitic peoples including the Amorites, Canaanites, and Phoenicians).

Plato — A Greek philosopher who lived between 427 and 347 B.C. He believed that actual things are copies of ideas that are beyond the limits of possible experience and knowledge. But they, in turn, are the objects of true knowledge. Philosophers are still trying to find solutions to the problems he posed in a number of philosophical discussions.

Plutarch — A Greek philosopher and historian who lived between 46 and 126 A.D. He taught and wrote in both Greece and Rome. His biographies, though often too moralizing (about "good" men and "bad" men) for modern scholars, are the source of much of our knowledge about both Greek and Roman "great" men.

Pompey — A great Roman General and statesman from 106 to 48 B.C.

Poop deck — A partial deck above the ship's main afterdeck.

Poseidon — The Greek god of the sea.

Priest — A male member of a religious body who performs sacred rites and other duties.

Priestess — A female member of a religious body authorized to perform sacred rites and duties.

Proconsul — A governor or military commander of a Roman province.

Protestant — A Christian denying the universal authority of the Pope.

Ptolemaic — Of or relating to the Ptolemies, a dynastic family who ruled Egypt after the death of Alexander the Great.

R

Ramses II — The King of Egypt from 1301 to 1235 B.C. He was a great builder who defeated the Hittites in 1280 B.C. at the Battle of Kadesh.

Ramses III — A King of Egypt who reigned from 1198 to 1166 B.C. He held off the attack of the "Sea Peoples" and built the temple of Medinet Habu which has reliefs depicting this victory.

Renan, Ernest — A French scholar sent to Lebanon by Napoleon III; author of "Mission to Phoenicia."

Reshef — The Canaanite god of war, the storm and pestilence.

142

Rib Addi — A local prince who ruled Byblos during the period of Hyksos control. He lived during the rule of the Egyptian Pharaoh, Akhnaton, in the Late Bronze Age.

Roman law — The legal system of the ancient Romans, including written and unwritten law. It is composed of many different elements; the traditional law of Rome, assembly legislation, codes of the Emperors, etc.

Roman period — From 64 B.C. to 330 A.D., relating to the time when the Romans took control of Byblos and Byblos became Roman in architecture, arts and thought.

Rubbing — An image obtained by placing paper on a raised or incised surface and rubbing the paper with a pencil, graphite or a crayon.

S

Saracen — A nomadic people who lived in the deserts between Syria and Arabia.

Sarcophagus — A coffin, usually made of stone. Sometimes beautifully carved or inscribed. They may be of limestone or marble. Those of the Egyptian pharaohs were often made of granite.

Satrap — A ruler or governor of a Persian satrapy (a state) who is subject to the authority or control of a higher official.

Satrapy — The Persian name for province or state.

Sayfas — A group of terrorists during the Ottoman period.

Schawarma — An Arab dish consisting of layers of lamb grilled on a skewer.

Scribe — One of a learned class of people that served to study, copy, edit and write manuscripts.

Semitic — A name that is applied to a native speaker of Arabic, Hebrew, and related languages. Other Semitic peoples of ancient times include the Babylonians, Assyrians, Aramaeans, Canaanites, and Phoenicians.

Service taxi — A public taxi operating as a bus along a fixed route, without a fixed schedule.

Seth — An ancient Egyptian god who was represented as evil, murderer of Osiris. Often he took on the form of a creature with the body of a greyhound with a long stiff tail, a thin curved muzzle, almond eyes, and long straight pointed ears. He is also represented as a pig, a hippopotamus, and an ant-eater.

Shaft tomb — A deep rock-cut tomb.

Shish Kebab — Lamb chunks cooked on skewers.

Sickle — A crescent-shaped agricultural tool with a short handle used for reaping grains.

Sidon — A port city located in Lebanon south of Beirut. One of the chief cities of Phoenicia.

Sigloi (pl.) — *Siglos (sing.)* — A Persian silver coin weighing about 5.6 grams.

Site — A place where human beings have established themselves, even momentarily; any place of human activity.

Site plan — A scale drawing that shows the topographic nature of the site and site control datum points.

Souk or suk — A bazaar; in Byblos these are partially roofed and arcaded.

Spear — A thrusting or throwing weapon with a long shaft and sharp blade.

Stone Age — The earliest period of human culture known. Characterized by the use of stone tools, it is sometimes known as the Palaeolithic. In Byblos, only the later subdivisions of this period were found, the Neolithic or New Stone Age, and the Chalcolithic or the Copper-Stone Age.

Sultan Selim I — An Ottoman Turkish ruler.

Surveyor — One of the most important members of an archaeological team. This person measures the area, form and position of various features of an archaeological site. The surveyor is the first to record the site before excavation and the last to leave it after excavation.

Syndicate — A group of people who form a group to carry out a particular type of business.

Syria — In antiquity a region in southwestern Asia bordering on the Mediterranean and including modern Syria, Lebanon, Israel and Jordan.

Syriac — A literary language based on eastern Aramaic.

T

Tabbouleh — An Arab salad consisting of finely chopped parsley, tomatoes, mint, cracked wheat, and onions with a dressing of lemon juice and olive oil.

Tamarisk — A desert shrub that can grow to be quite large.

Tell — An artificially created, usually flat-topped mound.

Temper — Particles of organic (wheat stalks) and/or inorganic (stone, grog) matter that is kneaded into clay to make the clay stiffer and harder.

Templars — Knights of a religious military order established in Jerusalem in the 12th century A.D. for the protection of pilgrims and the Holy Sepulchre.

Temple — A building reserved for religious purposes.

Tepidarium — One of the rooms in a Roman bath with lukewarm water.

Terracotta — Baked earth, generally used to describe fired pottery or architectural elements constructed of baked brick.

Thebes — A city in Upper Egypt which was the capital and religious center of Egypt during the 2nd millennium B.C.

Thutmoses I — 1530 to 1520 B.C. Son of Amenophis I, he was the first great conqueror of Egypt's New Kingdom.

Thutmoses II — 1520-1504 B.C. Son of Thutmoses I, he was a great warrior and the first husband of Queen Hatshepsut.

Thutmoses III — 1504 to 1450 B.C. King who was known as the Napoleon of Egypt. Using brilliant war tactics, he was responsible for gaining mastery over much of Syria and Palestine. He was also a great builder of monumental buildings, particularly those at Karnak.

Tric trac — Backgammon, a game.

Tripoli — A port city north of Byblos in north Lebanon.

Turk — An inhabitant of Turkey. A Moslem subject of the Turkish sultan.

Two-wheeled chariot — Earlier warfare in Mesopotamia and Syria had used the clumsy four-wheeled chariot. The lighter, faster two-wheeled vehicle proved a tremendous advantage. Egypt, of course, having no use for horses because it used the Nile for troop movements, had used only foot soldiers up to the time after the Hyksos.

V

Vassal state — A feudal state under the protection or submission of another state.

Vessel — A vase, cup, or bowl used as a container.

W

Wadi — The Arabic word meaning stream or river.

Water pipe — Also known as "hubbly-bubbly" or "narghilé" in Arabic. A tobacco smoking device consisting of a bowl mounted on a vessel of water; it is provided with a long tube so that the smoke is drawn through the water and up the tube to the mouth.

Wenamon — An official of the Temple of Amon at Karnak in about 1100 B.C. This unfortunate messenger of the Pharaoh spent many an unhappy day in the Byblos port.

Worry beads — A string of beads fingered by men in the Middle East to keep their hands busy. It is like a rosary with beads for the 99 names of God. Its strict use is to pronounce these names as one fingers the beads.

X

Xerxes I — The Great Persian King who ruled from 486 to 465 B.C.

Y

Yehowmilk — A King of Byblos during the Persian period.

Z

Zakar-Baal — A King of Byblos who sent Wenamon away from the city.

Zeus — The Greek god who is King of both gods and men.

145

Imprimerie Catholique sal
Araya, Lebanon
1988

Designed by
Jean Kartbaoui MSTD, DATD

BLACK S

CARTHAGE

MEDITERRANEAN SEA

CAIRO

N
W   E
S